THE RULES
&
SHORT STORIES

PHILIPPE NEWBY

Print2Demand Ltd

THE RULES & SHORT STORIES
Copyright © Philippe Newby & Charlotte Newby 2020

All Rights Reserved

First Published in April 2020 by
Print2Demand Ltd

Printed and bound in Great Britain by
www.print2demand.co.uk
Silsoe and Hastings

THE RULES
&
SHORT STORIES

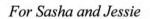

For Sasha and Jessie

Contents

Foreword

Reflections

1. The Rules

2. The Lag

3. To No Man But The King

4. History is Written…

5. Andy is Bob - Give or Take

6. Being Disabled Sucks

7. Extracts from *28 Days in Kerala*

8. Extracts from *Innocent Lives*

9. Sundries

Cogitations

10. Don't Mention the Boomies

11. To Be or Not To Be

Foreword
By Olive Travers

There is an ancient Greek proverb that states, "*Society grows great when old men plant trees whose shade they know they shall never sit in*". How then do we measure the actions of a man who responds to the devastating diagnosis of a terminal illness by planting a nuttery of different species of trees in the public car park beside his home? After that shattering diagnosis of Motor Neurone Disease (MND), Phil Newby, then 43, was told to go home, sort out his affairs and spend the few years at most that he had left with his wife Charlotte and his eleven and nine-year-old daughters. He not only did this but continued to face the existential crises of his diagnosis by living his life as one of engagement, connectivity, meaning and self-fulfilment.

Now, almost six years after the diagnosis, in this luminous new collection of his writings, *The Rules*, Phil Newby demonstrates his continuing capacity to engage with the meaning of both his past and present experiences with imagination, courage and creativity. In the wide reach of memoir, observational and opinion pieces between these covers, he is funny, sometimes mercilessly skewering and irreverent but always with verve, wit and compassion. The disparate pieces are united by the Rules of the title, how rules are interpreted by individuals and different societies depending on the randomness of where in the world the stork dropped us. Phil's own introduction to *The Rules* is a Monty Python-esque description of the debacle of how to get an essential battery for his mobility scooter out of the country for a family holiday. The source of Phil's own relaxed attitude towards bureaucratic rules becomes clear in the colourful parade of his French mother's family; grandparents, uncles and cousins, who flaunted petty rules with panache, leading to a hilarious account of the backfiring of his attempt to recreate the halcyon childhood memories of his French mother breezing through customs in Dover laden down with contraband goods, with his own children and law-abiding wife.

In the short extracts from his 2017 *Innocent Lives* novella, we see this French side of his family and their rural community in a different context of rules in the nail-biting descriptions of their plight, whilst under Nazi occupation during the war.

The Lag is an extraordinarily visceral description of the lawlessness of a mud fight in which Harry Potter meets Lord of the Flies at a remote, medieval-sounding Christian charity boarding school. Phil attended this school set up for orphaned inner-city children when it provided for the no longer well-off, like his now single mother, to source a free, good education for him.
He turns to adults in two affectionate and sharply observed pieces about different attitudes to rules in different generations. Through his charming, if irresponsible airline pilot father, he traces the fun, exotic era of the growth of air travel, while Charlotte's war hero grandfather epitomises the quiet, stoic patriotism of adhering to one's duty as being the only rule to be kept.

It is when Phil writes about his own experiences that he echoes the late, witty and waspish A. A. Gill's *"If you say something is beyond humour, it is beyond human experience"*. In extracts from *28 Days in Kerala*, his first stay in an Ayurvedic Indian hospital, all the rules of conventional hospital treatment are turned on their heads leading to laugh-out-loud accounts of him as a very bewildered Englishman being subjected to a barrage of enemas.

The brutally honest *Being Disabled Sucks* shows how the lens through which Phil views the world has changed over the past six years. He recalls his own part in the casual insensitivity to those with disability which he now encounters and how an anecdote from work about the humiliation of a difficult colleague with disability had, in the past, been at the top of his repertoire of funny stories. Another lens that has changed is the one given to him in business school - never to give anything away without getting something back. This view has been radically upturned by the kindness of others he is now experiencing and which he details in his many "lump in the throat" moments.

To be truly human is to bear the burden of our own mortality and to strive to help others carry theirs. The ultimate *rules* challenged in this book are those of the current legislation which deny him and so many others the comfort of knowing they can be assisted in dying at a time of their own choosing. Here, on the remote west coast of Ireland where I live among the Celts, we believe that we "do death well", and that a good death is one where we die at home in a peaceful and dignified way surrounded by our nearest and dearest. Phil wants nothing more than this. He is not one to shirk a challenge, as his hobbit-style home built into the side of a hill attests. It was still a leap of courage for him to take on a legal challenge to the current UK legislation on assisted dying only to experience, after a demanding full year of work, it being rejected first by the High Court and then the Court of Appeal. Undaunted, he continues to use his voice to do media work and lobby MPs. In the appendix, To Be Or Not To Be, he succinctly argues his position on the rules that are even present in dying.

As Phil goes out on his mobility scooter and sees the trees in Newby's Nuttery taking root, he is acutely aware of how his body continues to shed its powers like a snake shedding skin and how the home that he and Charlotte have created for their family has been violated by the bulky accoutrements of disability aids.

Phil demonstrates in this collection of writings how to be brave in a time of sorrow. By his grasp of all our finiteness he shows how his relationships - with life, with other people, and with nature - are what give meaning.

Phil *has* adopted Churchill's rule to "keep plodding on", (though this is not how he expresses it). In *The Rules* he has created something that will enlarge the lives of all who read it.

Reflections

The Rules

Part 1: The Battery

It is not essential to the narrative that follows, but I started
to become increasingly physically disabled with something
nasty in about 2015. By 2018 planning a vacation came
with all the thrill that you might get if asked to risk-assess a
primary school visit to an abattoir. As torturing myself is a
recognised pastime in our house, this same year I'd settled
on taking our little family to The Gambia - a country that it
turns out has no healthcare system and apparently no
established way for a wheelchair passenger to alight from
an aeroplane. This news was alarming and charming to me
in equal measure, because it might set the tone for one of
those truly memorable family holidays. My wife Charlie
was unnerved by the prospect and our teenage girls, Sasha
and Jessie, were perplexed enough by their dad's decision,
for me to conclude that this Russian-roulette holiday choice
had the edge over lying on a lounger in Tenerife.
Going abroad with limited movement and in a wheelchair is
a 'challenge'. The corruption of this word means it is now
just a euphemism used by positive folk to describe a shit-
storm of admin, accompanied by a catalogue of minor
humiliations. A second word 'special' is then deployed as
an accomplice (also against its own will) and used as a
form of garnish, in an attempt to mask just how

incompatible you've become with the smooth running of the normal world. So boxes have to be ticked for special assistance, special menus and special insurance has to be procured, when really the word special should just be substituted for awkward.

The plan was to take a tiny folding electric mobility scooter on the trip in lieu of a wheelchair, giving everyone one less heavy inanimate object to push and pull, whilst giving me greater autonomy. The hope was that I'd be transformed by this mode of transport from luggage to an engaging travelling companion. The scooter was air-safe, or so it said on the box, which meant that with the help of an aeroplane it could fly. We duly sent off the measurements and spec. to the airport and then to the airline only to receive a response requesting the Materials Safety Data Sheet for the scooter. A long search on the internet led me to a manufacturer in Guangzhou, enabling the download of a pidgin English data sheet, confirming that there was nothing weapons-grade about the scooter. This was a disappointment as I'd been hoping to discover the button that unleashed the Sidewinder missiles, but importantly, the airline now seemed satisfied. As the scooter had a temperamental battery, I had agreed with Charlie that, as a precaution, we must replace it for a new one before travelling. Charlie packaged the old battery carefully, but then as is her way, went to check the rules on posting batteries. I winced as she read out the Catch 22 protocol for batteries in transit and sensed the stirring of a powerful, latent anger. I'm not sure if this anger that bubbles in the deep is a primeval rage of a caveman trapped in a modern world, or of a toddler who has just been denied gummy bears at a supermarket checkout, but I know from scanning the terrifying comments pages of the Daily Mail On-line, that it must be an emotion shared by many a red-faced Englishman. To put it another way, hearing the rules on posting batteries brought out the Donald Trump.

The rules for posting batteries are as follows: You can't. The Royal Mail has helpfully compiled a long web page on the subject that includes a seven-point protocol that must, in law, be followed when really the page should just flash red with the words: You Can't. The only subtle addition might be an asterisk, which points to a small print foot-note that says: But everyone does. Our argument at home played out as follows with Charlie opening the batting,

"It says here that you can't send the battery away to get a replacement".

"But I could go online and buy a new one from any one of a thousand places and have it posted home right now."

"They do this for a reason."

"Oh no they don't."

"Well don't you think it might be about safety?"

"No, no, no, it's just the self-same guys who have insisted that the words - may contain nuts - is stamped on bags of peanuts getting their kicks again."

"It says here it's about the risk of short circuits and fire and fumes and that the post office will destroy it if you are caught posting it."

"For the love of God. We've just got an airline to agree that the same battery can travel on a Boeing at 39,000 feet doing 500 miles per hour. Don't you think it's alright for it to be put on a delivery truck and sent up the M6?"

"OK, as ever, you seem to be an expert, but it's the rules, it's illegal and I'm not going to post it for you."

Charlie and I have got pretty good at squabbling over the years, as the same patterns of irritation at each other play themselves out in almost identical spats against one new

5

topic or another. The scooter battery kerfuffle was just another addition to an ongoing skirmish about our differing approach to rules. Unfortunately, our girls fall in line with their mother when it comes to rules. As a result, it's both childish and exhilarating for me to freak my band of snowflakes out, simply by driving against the arrows in a shopping centre car park.

Due to her approach to the rules however, Charlie has never been ripped off buying second hand equipment, had a non-paying tenant with no lease outstay his welcome for eighteen months, or been caught climbing on the roof of a building society. But she has had to pick up the pieces of each event with me. Such is her goodness that she still blushes if I mention the great tangerine heist of 2014, when she was pulled up in the supermarket self-scan section and busted for failing to scan a bag of oranges. I was as delighted for her as she was mortified. More recently in 2018, Charlie was caught speeding, doing thirty-four in a thirty mile an hour limit, but angrily rejects this as evidence that over time she is succumbing to the dark side and becoming the Bonnie to my Clyde.

Rules and laws obviously play a big part in making a civilised world that can tick along, but despite their importance, our attitude towards them seems to vary a great deal. For some, they provide crucial demarcation lines between what is right and what is wrong, for others they are there to be bent through personal interpretation, others still see the rule book only as an à la carte menu to choose from, whilst a small minority want nothing to do with them whatsoever. Meanwhile, I'm left wondering if Charlie's and my different views on obeying rules come from our upbringings or from somewhere deeper in our respective natures?

Part 2: Cross-Channel Smuggling

Every summer of our childhood my Mum, sister Annabel and I travelled by road to France to see our family. Whilst there we would collect or be given contraband. Most was in the form of food or alcohol, but for several years my particular thing was amassing large quantities of fireworks to bring home and sell to friends. These were mainly firecrackers and bangers that were wrapped in a thin red greaseproof paper. They could be bought at any toyshop or Bar Tabac. Each was bound by a white sticker showing the face of a tiger surrounded by Chinese script and even the largest variety, which looked very much like four cartoon sticks of dynamite, only cost a few centimes. One year, on a day visit to a marvellous new invention called a hypermarket, we fell in love with the terrapins that were for sale in a tank in the pet aisle. They were babies each about the size of half a boiled egg and we bought four on a whim. I petted them all holiday feeding them pieces of mince and attempting to get them to inflict wounds on my sister. Then the day came when we had to pack up our things into our Fiat and make the twelve-hour journey home. As usual, bottles of fortified wine and strong spirits were hidden in the foot wells and around the spare tyre and amongst the clothes in our suitcases. Then boxes of wine were added for good measure, making the little car sit back on its rear wheels. Cheeses and meats were wrapped in newspaper and placed with an ice block somewhere in the middle of the boot. My fireworks would be squeezed into any available space all around the car. Some of this could be done the night before leaving, but early in the morning before saying our goodbyes, Mamie would usually present us with several more bags of fresh vegetables and cheeses to somehow cram into the dangerously overloaded car, before we beeped the horn and left for England.

On arrival at the ferry port in Calais, Mum would breezily smile at French passport control. Placed at eye level I could survey the icons on the warning signs that listed all the items it was prohibited to take back across the Channel. This particular year, I had a Walls ice cream tub on my lap in the front seat, which was half full of water and half full of terrapins. It was, I remember, an excellent year, because save for a firearm, we had close to a full house as I checked off each illegal item on the poster against the mental list of what we had around our feet and in the boot.

The ferry journey was generally a pleasure and the supposedly serious business of British passport control and then customs never troubled us. A pretty single mother driving a red Fiat Panda, with two happy-go-lucky kids in tow, seemed enough for us to be waved through. Mum would point to a mirror glass wall that faced down from a building at Dover port, under which all traffic had to travel. Beyond it lay parking bays where businessmen, hippies and untidy people who looked like criminals were having the contents of their cars removed by customs officers. She would say,

"Just look up into that mirrored building and smile," explaining that this is the building where spotters look out on the cars and identify the suspicious people who need to be pulled over. It's never really occurred to me, but on reflection we were a pretty hot team and if circumstances had been different and we had grown up in Miami, with family in Colombia, we could have made some big money.

The family's first foray into moving illegal product across the Channel, through Dover, had come some seventeen years earlier. Back in the spring of 1964, my Mum and Dad were due to be married. A small reception was planned at a village pub in Sussex. Somehow it was agreed that my French grandparents, Mamie and Pépé, would bring the meat for the wedding breakfast. The 'somehow' most likely came in the form of Pépé, who fearing poisoning or starvation in England, instructed Mamie to make the offer of meat. Neither had ever been abroad before, so the long trip by train to Sussex via Orleans, Paris, Calais, Dover, London and then on to Horsham was a major event, even before factoring in the prospect of their first born child marrying an Englishman.

As far as I know, the French leg of the overnight journey went without incident and by early morning of the second day my bleary-eyed grandparents had made it to Dover and were re-boarding a stopping train bound for Waterloo station. Their second class compartment was initially empty, so they installed themselves in comfort, placing their heavy luggage on the overhead racks in front of them. The train began its London bound journey picking up the morning commuters. Mamie and Pépé watched with interest as the bureaucrats and business people of the stockbroker belt filled their carriage and compartment, wearing suits and hats and clutching briefcases, umbrellas and folded newspapers. They listened in curiosity to the odd exchanges of an unfamiliar language that they could not speak.

As they approached the outskirts of the metropolis, I expect that they might have been a little nervous, facing the prospect of crossing the capital city of a foreign country, but their state of mild anxiety was not reduced by the sight of a crimson drip from the luggage rack falling onto the commuter that faced them. Her eyes widening, Mamie

9

nudged Pépé and whispered something as they tried not to stare at the commuter opposite them, who stared impassively back - lost in the daily ritual of his morning's journey. To their mounting horror, a second drip landed on the shoulder of his overcoat and then a third. The meat in the suitcase was beginning to give up its juices. Though the morning was still relatively cool, Pépé began to sweat. As the train disgorged its passengers along the platform at Waterloo, Mamie and Pépé stayed back waiting for their compartment to clear, before letting out a sigh and a joint chuckle. They had got away with it. Furtively, Pépé kept watch for the train guard and platform attendants whilst Mamie retrieved the leaking meat suitcase and opened it. The sight was not a pretty one. Blood from the carefully wrapped contents had penetrated its packaging, soaked into the lining of the case and had begun to soften the thin brown leather, creating a ruddy bloom on the outside. But worse, it was finding its way out around the stiff leather corner caps. There was nothing to be done, so she closed it up again. Discarding the case or its contents was not an option. It was too great a treasure to leave behind. If they had abandoned the bloody suitcase it might have caused an incident involving a lurid headline in the Evening Standard about a suspected torso in a suitcase on a Kent bound train. So one of the pair, most likely Mamie, picked it up by the handle and they continued their onward journey. The situation was not about to improve. As Pépé carried the suitcase through the tiled concourse at Victoria Station, it began to leave a trail of blood. There, they settled cautiously into their Horsham bound train, like a pair of mild-mannered axe murderers.

Part 3: Les Girolles

My French family took a very relaxed view on many other things including seat belts, speeding, smoking in undesignated places, peeing in undesignated places and trespassing. There's nothing particularly criminal in this law breaking, it's just the simple result of ordinary folk who don't enjoy the encumbrance of too many rules. It would have taken a seismic event to stop my uncles from having an aperitif and glass of wine at lunch, despite the low blood-to-alcohol drink driving threshold, but who can blame them when Air France pilots were still getting wine with their in-flight meals well into the twenty first century. There is a distant memory floating in the leaky receptacle between my ears. I'm sitting on the back rack of a bicycle aged five. Pépé and my uncles are cycling in a line along one of the straight, Roman roads that leave Lamotte and point into the forests. Our swarthy group stops at an entrance and the men lift a gate to a sandy track, dropping their bikes into the springy, purple heather and long grass of the verge, scattering the crickets. I'm passed across a dry ditch by strong arms and we push our way into the scrub. They shush me when I talk and it occurs to my junior mind that they are right, because as anyone knows, hunting is a stealthy activity. The men fan out and start padding through the leaf mould. After a while at a glade formed by a cluster of midget, gnarled oaks, someone stops to examine the fallen leaves, pulling a small orange object from the ground and putting it in a bag. Heads down, we all begin to scuff about in the leaf litter, pulling up the squishy yellow, orange trumpets wherever we find them, before moving on to another similar spot along the dried-out shore of a large shallow pond. All this happens in near silence, which is

11

quite natural, because this group of intrepid men (of which I am a very proud guest member) is on a hunt.

In later life it occurred, in a flash of brilliance, that stalking game differs from picking mushrooms in a couple of striking ways. Mushrooms, it turns out, don't need to be stalked. They don't get spooked or sniff you out if you are downwind of them, nor as far as I'm aware do they charge if cornered. Mushrooms have neither burrows for protection nor wings for escape. That afternoon, like primitive man, we were only in the middle of the food chain. Much as our very distant ancestors, we were creeping around gathering food whilst avoiding the apex predators. In this case, these happened to be the landowner or worse, the gamekeeper.

In the old days, I reckon that Mamie and Pépé and their neighbours took flora and fauna from the woods with a revolutionary zeal. The wooded private estates of châteaux covered most of the area, the majority owned by minor aristocrats or business people who resided in Paris and came to hunt only occasionally, leaving their lands mostly in the hands of caretakers and gamekeepers. That late summer's day, our quarry was the girolle mushroom, which was as prized then as it is now. Back then, estate owners would have had the first mushrooms picked fresh and sent immediately to their homes in Paris, as soon as they poked their little orangey heads above the leaves. The bulk would be kept preserved, like thousands of little brains, in Kilner jars for adding to meat stews over the winter months. The locals only wanted a piece of this action. It was never on offer, so they just quietly took it.

Times have changed, or so I thought, when one day more recently my cousin's boyfriend Miké asked me along to gather girolles on some woodland that he had leased for his

peat business. We stepped out early one morning onto a concrete hard standing where Miké kept his diggers and looked out into the bracken understory beneath tall pine trees. He handed me a pair of supermarket carrier bags and rolled a cigarette whilst considering our plan. We struck out first along a track, cutting into the woods across the mossy ground in search of the leafy, loamy, dampish conditions in which girolles enjoy growing. Occasionally Miké would stop to show aspects of his work in the woods. After an hour of scouring, we only had a couple of dozen baby mushrooms swinging at the bottom of our bags. At his instruction, we then jumped a ditch half full with black water and squelched through an area of wet woodland, before emerging again into bracken and sunlight, shaded by occasional silver birch and holly trees. A sandy track ran nearby. Occasionally, Miké would stop and sniff the wind a little, which I assumed to be some kind of countryman's mushroom radar in operation. By now a little bored, I chatted away whilst keeping a cursory eye on the ground. Then Miké suddenly turned palms up with an expression that implored me to shut up. He listened for a second and then hissed,
"Get down!"
We both dropped face down onto the forest floor. Twisting my head and exhaling a couple of leaves out of my vision, I saw a smart blue saloon car pass by on the track, separated from us by only a thin band of bracken. We lay in silence for a second, before Miké got up onto his knees to check that the danger had passed. As we dusted ourselves off, he explained that we had been lucky that our close call had been with an elderly château owner and not his short-tempered gamekeeper. No apology was offered by Miké,

but none was needed, because my grandpa and uncles had got me into trespassing forty years earlier.

Back in more revolutionary times, John Jacques Rousseau penned the memorable quote: "When the people shall have nothing more to eat, they will eat the rich".

I don't subscribe to the "Eat the Rich" slogan of modern day scary lefties, but remain very much in favour of eating their mushrooms. In fact, last summer marked the zenith of this long standing, but occasional hankering for mushroom thievery. On a day out to visit the Sandringham Estate in Norfolk, we eyed two tempting spherical objects on the south lawn of the house. Though distant, a little further scoping out confirmed that they were puffballs. These kings-of-mushrooms had chosen to grow on the Queen of England's front lawn beside a lone spruce tree. I lifted the front wheels of the tiny electric mobility scooter over the edging from the path to the grass and like a bear on a tricycle, set off towards the tree. The scooter bore down on the mushrooms somewhere close to its top speed of 4mph. Obviously startled at the audacity of it all, the mushrooms put up little resistance, allowing themselves to be plucked from the ground and bagged up swiftly, whereupon I beat a hasty retreat to the other side of the south lawn and re-joined the footpath. The next morning, shrouded in a miasma of fried mushroom smoke, I triumphantly ate the pair whilst humming the Internationale.

Poaching, trespass and foraging were really just the perks of being a working class family in La Sologne, no different from mum coming home with biscuits from a job in the biscuit factory. Many, perhaps most families on the Rue Pierre Fournier in Lamotte Beuvron were of similar dispositions, but as far as I know they also paid their taxes and lived in a world that was by and large free from burglaries, theft, robberies, mugging, litter and save for the occasional tanglings with the Catholic Church - sex attacks. Front doors, garages and cars were generally left unlocked, policemen were obeyed and the professional class was begrudgingly respected. It was only really in the nineties when urban crime, as we know it today, arrived. Mamie's outside cook-house was burgled - no insurances paid out - so slowly houses, outbuildings and cars were respectively bolted and locked.

When they were newlywed teenagers, the war and the four years of Nazi occupation that resulted, must have taught my grandparents a great deal about the necessity of obeying the rules on the face of things - to avoid deportation, whilst breaking them on the quiet - for survival. The same dark chapter brought them face to face with violence and atrocity. On reflection, it is not so surprising that when their next door neighbour shot his wife in the mid-nineties, they were not traumatised by the event. By the time we arrived in France on our summer holidays, this tragedy was conveyed to us as a no-big-deal incident, though it had happened just across the adjoining walls of their four roomed home.

Their neighbours had always kept themselves to themselves, but both would smile and wave at me and Annabel across the rusty chain link, when we ventured into Pépé's vegetable garden to play as children. To me they appeared a little mysterious, mainly because as I remember it, they waved but did not speak. This is no crime in itself, especially as the yellow number plates on Mum's Fiat had already announced to the Rue Pierre Fournier that the English had arrived for their annual holiday.

15

However, I'd heard it said that the neighbours had all but moved out of their small house in favour of living in a breezeblock shed that backed onto Mamie's cook-house, though this was only hinted at by the large TV aerial sitting atop the pantiled roof. This added to my curiosity, as did whispered comments about their son being 'troubled'. The lady next door had begun to lose her mind to dementia and it's not certain if in turning a shotgun on her, her husband's act was one of violence, or of compassion. He was duly led to prison. A decade or so later, long after the next door garden had become waist high in grass, the son moved back to his parental home. His arrival was announced by nothing more than the twang of punk music across the thick adjoining walls. He was perhaps in his mid-thirties and, as a lonely drunk, he'd occasionally visit Mamie, when lonely and drunk. Mamie seemed unphased by Philippe's shuffling arrival, the smile that missed teeth, the black eye or by his large and surprisingly fearsome golden retriever.

Mamie was calm and courteous when he slurred and struggled to hold onto his temper. I watched more than once, smiling with alarm, as she snuffed out the sparks on the fuse of this human stick of dynamite, with nothing more than a bit of motherly love. Like her, I liked Philippe. I enjoyed chatting with him, but it came with the same exciting sensation one might get if you stuck your whole arm through the bars of a tiger's cage. He was OK though, with good taste in music and a broad worldview, and if you could have ignored the fact that he was alone and drinking himself to death in the same small house where his father had killed his mother, all would have been well.

As an occasional visitor to the street, like an extra in a movie, I did nothing to help. Others I think might have

16

done. The first time I met Philippe at the gateway to Mamie's house, I asked him the name of his dog.

"She's called Blondie," he replied.

It was a good name for a golden retriever granted, but as we sat and drank a bottle of Heineken together, a little voice in my head said,

"Hold on... wasn't that the name of Hitler's dog?"

Part 4: Uncle Michel and Uncle Jean-Lou

My uncle Michel, a taciturn man with a stern face, perfected an unusual minor illegal activity that took the form of illicit, al-fresco butchery. His garage was lined with freezers and a roll of very large butchers' knives lived on a countertop, giving the space a serial killer vibe. In La Sologne the correct course of action if one was unfortunate enough to hit a large wild animal whilst driving was to call the police, who would log the incident and offer the four-legged victim back to the owner of the estate from which it had sprung. In Lamotte-Beuvron and its environs, the other course of action was to call Michel. Like a hick version of Winston Wolf from the Tarantino movie, Uncle Michel's home phone might ring during the middle of dinner. He would converse quietly, take directions, make apologies, put on a coat and leave via the door to the garage, picking his knives from the counter as he passed.

He would get to the spot of the incident, sometimes in the dark, and butcher the life-expired animal on the hoof. As plunging large knives into a big carcass on a darkened road verge in dense woodland is likely to create a sense of unease amongst passing motorists, Michel would have to move at speed. A smaller animal might be dragged out of

17

sight, or moved altogether for processing, but bearing in mind that an adult red deer might weigh well over a hundred kilos, Michel would have to work deftly, building up a sweat when dealing with such a beast, in the place and position that it had fallen. Though it's the stuff of nightmares, it is not hard to conjure the exquisite mental image of a happy urban family staying at the nearby Centre Parcs resort, driving through the forest at night. They are all talking cheerfully over the music that's playing on the radio as they round a bend. Then, caught in the headlights, knelt over Bambi's mum is the tableau of my deadpan uncle, sweat dripping from his brow, as he lifts a bloody hand from the offal to shield his dazzled eyes, only to reveal the glint of a large, stained blade.

The poor unfortunate animal would generally be split several ways, with Michel returning home with huge slabs of on-the-bone meat for further dissection on the way to his freezers. As a result of his ninja butchery, family barbeques had a medieval and sometimes bowel-blocking quality about them.

Uncle Jean-Lou is unusual in our family. For starters his Christian name is uncommon. Fable has it that as a new-born, he was named Jean-Louis by a visiting Italian neighbour after Mamie and Pépé refused to - in irritation at having had three baby boys on the trot. Though this may have seemed like an inauspicious start in life, his irrepressible élan was not to be dampened. As a naughty toddler, Pépé would scold him and threaten malevolently to put him in a sack, add bricks and throw him into the canal. The tiny man-child would draw himself to full height, fold his arms defiantly and mime to his unnerved dad just how he'd tear his way out of the sack with his teeth, before swimming to the surface and seeking retribution.

Amongst a family of dark haired, brown eyed and tanned skinned people he was a lone throw-back in being blonde and as he grew older and stronger, he developed the larger than life facial features that he shares with other Frenchmen like Gérard Depardieu. Whilst there can be a certain dour quality to his brothers, Jean-Lou fizzes with a mischief that is only rivalled by his unreliability. His tall stories are legendary, but such is his charm that you can never be quite sure that he did not indeed water ski with Silvio Berlusconi, disco-dance with Cher or scuba dive with Jacques Cousteau. He rarely arrives in the same vehicle as last time and only occasionally with the same girlfriend. Though he may arrive by long wheelbase van, tipper-truck, performance motorbike or fast BMW, there is a dead certainty that his new girlfriend will be blonde. At a family celebration, Jean-Lou may promise to bring the Champagne, or the starter, or the desert and not turn up at all. This will cause little fuss as given the odds are below 50/50, someone more reliable will have made a contingency for him. One fairly recent summer he promised to bring a fish starter to a family meal but, when by lunchtime he'd not shown, spicy merguez sausages were rolled onto an oil drum barbeque and were being turned by my Uncle Daniel, when Jean-Lou, driving a battered Saab, sped into the courtyard in a plume of dust. Never one to rush on foot, he opened the door and sauntered to the boot, which sagged a little, whilst offering vague greetings and nonchalantly popping the lid. As it opened, the tail of a large sea creature flapped out over the rear bumper and began to fan in the hot breeze. Everyone already outside came out of the shade to inspect. We peered in and a very large unblinking eye, that absorbed all of our surprise, stared blankly back into the huddle of faces through its dead fish-eye lens. Our starter had arrived. Whilst others from the house came out and gathered around to pay homage, Jean-Lou talked into the air about the "magouille", or dodgy-dealing, that had led to him gaining custody of the giant fish. This could have involved something about a glazing job on a mini-submersible, a poker game at the aquarium, or a debt owed by a Japanese whaling captain, but frankly, we had all given up listening years ago.

It is no surprise that, having almost entirely rejected the concept of timekeeping, along with a range of other social norms, Jean-Lou's adherence to the rule of law is an occasional one. Though nothing close to a criminal, Jean-Lou fits quite happily into the 'dodgy' class of men. To use an Irish idiom, he's the kind of fella who would be able to give you three threes in change for a £9 note. After a chequered career as a tradesman that covered amongst other things, commercial floor laying, conservatory extensions and property development, Jean-Lou bought a small fast food joint in Sully-sur-Loire that does Pizza delivery. It was named Speezza in an ingenious car-crash of the words 'Speed' and 'Pizza'. By his own cheerful admission, Jean-Lou knew very little about food preparation, but energetically explained that no knowledge whatsoever was needed. According to him, the greatest test of his skill was estimating how many pats of frozen dough to move from the freezer to defrost ahead of the evening service. To our surprise, all started well and Jean-Lou won us, his toughest critics, over by inviting any one of us behind the counter to construct our own pizzas. This was a no-holds-barred affair, allowing the very young and old alike to don loose blue gloves, roll out our dough and experiment unsupervised with flavour combinations of our own making. Like nursery school kids during 'messy play' Jean-Lou would encourage us to do our worst, so we'd dip our hands into watery tubs underneath the counter and get creative with blue cheese, anchovies and pepperoni. Jean Lou had hired an assistant manager, who also almost predictably, knew nothing about pizzas either. This young man spent much of his day sitting with his laptop at a small table by the drinks chiller, designing a stock-market algorithm that was set to make himself and his boss Jean-Lou, fantastically and improbably rich.

Speezza sits on one side of a once charming market square just outside the tranquil, pedestrianised beauty of Sully-sur-Loire. The road across the old marketplace serves as a main trunk route into the town. Over time traffic fumes have blackened the fine stone structures that Jean-Lou and his team look out onto. Directly facing him is a handsome building that looks as though it might have once been the town hall, but is actually the police station. As in picturesque market towns in England, this once impressive building is now untidy and the station within has shrunk and shrunk over the years. However, the national police have made use of the space, by turning the upper floors and the stable courtyard behind it into accommodation for newly commissioned officers. Initially, this provided Jean-Lou with a captive audience of young and hungry professionals, who worked shifts and when finished, sought Speezza out for pizzas.

Relations were apparently very cordial with the neighbouring cops, but then a chain of foreseeable events started to make the pizza delivery business a little more tricky. Speezza had planning conditions attached to it that

21

restricted it to take away pizzas and limited the opening hours with a strict closing time. It also came without a license to serve alcohol. Never one to be bothered by this sort of annoyance, Jean-Lou bought tables for the inside and for the pavement, closed whatever time of night the business became thin or he got sleepy, and started keeping wine in the chiller and pouring it for anyone who fancied a drop. Complaints were made by neighbours and the friendly local police popped over to nip the situation in the bud. Jean-Lou took the police lecture like a man, but undeterred, continued to operate as before. A further, sterner warning was given, but was duly ignored by the affable restaurateur from across the square. Irritated by this, the gendarmes started to keep watch on Speezza from the comfort of their living rooms across the road. A weary officer might look out of the window, then check the time on a phone, before crossing the square to catch Jean-Lou in the act of opening after hours, or serving customers at tables, or providing alcohol. On seeing an approaching policeman, Jean-Lou might tough things out, by charmingly explaining that all the diners were just friends and family, enjoying a private gathering after-hours. This is something to which his admiring customers would readily agree. Alternatively, and depending on his appetite for confrontation, on seeing a gendarme striding across the square, he might just grab a tabard and helmet, then jump onto a delivery scooter and squeal away into the town. Now in France, as elsewhere, the police did not tend to like it up 'em, so a different tack was taken and a trap was set. From across the road Jean-Lou was observed one night drinking rosé in the brightly lit takeaway and at closing his BMW was followed out of town, where he was pulled over by a squad car on suspicion of drink driving. Despite having developed the frame of bon-viveur, Jean-Lou is not a big drinker, so to their disappointment, he passed the breathalyser test with flying colours. What's more, his car was in good working order too, but on inspecting his driving licence closely, the local officers struck gold. It was a fake. Since late childhood, Jean-Lou had ridden or driven anything with handlebars or a steering wheel that he could get behind. As a result, he had at an early age, become a capable driver of cars, vans, trucks and motorbikes of all kinds, so he had dispensed with the requirement of taking a driving test and had bought a fake licence somewhere instead. It seems to have served him very well, because throughout my life Jean-Lou has crisscrossed France and the continent beyond with regularity, during work and at play. The intrepid police of Sully had taken down their man. A court appearance and a fine for Jean-Lou loomed, but to their frustration they were unable to take away his driving license, because he had never had one.

We made a pilgrimage to Speezza during the summer that followed this incident. I sat for a while chatting to Jean-Lou's deputy who explained, with resigned amusement beyond his years, that the cat and mouse game continued. For a short while after being pulled over, Jean-Lou relied on the bus or accepted lifts from friends to get him home, but soon wavered and started using the company vehicles as his preferred means of transport. He'd been caught again, this time on a Speezza delivery scooter, but rather than desisting he had upped his game instead. Sometimes both staff members now depart simultaneously at night with Jean-Lou by scooter. They swap outer clothing and act as decoys, hoping that their much-loved boss will make it back without getting his collar felt. The conversation with Jean-Lou's right hand man took place on a summer's evening. We were sitting outside Speezza, before its stipulated opening time in the fading sunshine, seated at a folding table. When he'd finished his story, the deputy manager smiled and raised his glass of wine in salute towards the police station.

Part 5: Magic the Cat

When our kids were little, Mum used to rent a gîte for all of us, for a week every summer. My sister Annabel and I had known this farmhouse when we were kids as it sat in a squat farmyard just a little further up the track from my Uncle Daniel and Auntie Marylene's factory and home. Jacqui, the red-faced farmer had died and his wife had passed away soon after. The farmhouse had been cleared, save for lumps of rustic furniture and was let out to holidaymakers. Despite this, the ghosts of the previous occupiers remained, looking out at the herd of Limousin cattle that grazed free-range on the tussocked meadows encircling the buildings. By then Mamie, now in her nineties, had been moved into my aunt and uncle's home and was living in a large studio room that served as an old people's home for her, but also as a day crèche for the most junior of her great grandchildren.

Our kids had nearly melted into their car seats by the time we drove into the open factory hangar of my aunt and uncle's house on a blistering summer's day, that marked the end of our twelve-hour journey from England and the beginning of our summer holiday. Their bodies made a Velcro swoosh as Charlie and I unshackled them from their little half cocoons in the back of the car. They sprang forward loosening their limbs, but stopped abruptly at the sight of Tyson, the monstrous grey-white bull terrier, who was lying snout-to-the-floor on the grey-white of the concrete in the middle of the hangar. He lay motionless in his camouflaged state with unblinking eyes adjusting only slightly towards us. Though our girls were nervous, it was obvious that the dog's mind was on other things as we stepped over the rope that restrained the mighty beast. I asked my Uncle Daniel what was up with Tyson. He just shrugged, saying that a stray kitten had moved in to a log pile just across the corrugated iron partition. For several days now Tyson had lain in wait, motionless like a crocodile, hoping for the little feline to make a fatal error by stepping into the arc of his territory. The girls were given some cat food and pointed in the direction of the log store, where a playful black and white kitten emerged from between a gap in the wood and accosted them. Every morning for the next three days we did the same, becoming increasingly fond of the little orphan.

On the evening of the fourth day, I went down for an aperitif with my aunt and uncle. The hangar was bathed in sunlight and Daniel squinted at me from a plastic chair as I arrived. We sat and chatted before Daniel recounted that he had crossed the hangar that afternoon, where by chance he had spotted Tyson's rear end sloping away towards the gap between his and my aunt's car. Fortunately, Daniel had done a double-take, because the beast happened to have the kitten dangling between its jaws. As Tyson already knew that he was in the wrong, Daniel had been able to coax the kitten out of the dog's mouth. It was clear that the kitten had suffered at least a broken leg, because it could not walk but though obviously badly damaged it was still conscious, so Daniel had put it up and out of reach on the top of the log store, next to some food and water. We went over and

found the little creature prostrate on its side high up on the log pile. It was in a state, but Daniel said philosophically, that time would tell and who knows what the outcome would be, because,
"Kittens are made of rubber".
I wandered back along the dusty track, wondering how to break the news to our little girls. We visited the next day and although the kitten could only drag itself on its front paws, found that it still had an appetite for food and for life. Without any prompting from our little ones I resolved to play God and quietly nipped into town to buy a cat box. Nobody on the Gallic side of my clan batted an eye-lid about the prospect of us taking the kitten back home to England. We had been on the lookout for a cat anyway, so what could be more natural? Charlie was less convinced, but a further week of holiday in Le Cher lay ahead, so nothing seemed terribly pressing.
We departed for the second stage of our holiday with instructions for Daniel to keep his hound away from the cat and an agreement that we would collect it by taking a detour on the way home. The kitten's recovery was almost miraculous, so a week later, following a pre-dawn departure, we were back in the hangar to collect it. A couple of days before, Charlie had begun to ask me the most salient questions. She wanted to know what my plan was and what might happen to us if stopped at customs in Dover, or what fate would befall the kitten? Having no real answers, I countered with bluff and bravado. I would sort things out and if anything went wrong, I'd manfully take the rap. The girls and I had already agreed a plan, but even by their infant standards, it was patchy. The most sophisticated element was using the frozen blue blocks from our cool-

box as an emergency cat coolant in the event that we had to leave the car in the sun with the kitten on board.

The kitten was placed in its box between the girls' car seats, providing instant entertainment for the long journey and we were sent off by our French family with hugs and kisses.

All went well through the long morning, though the tension went up a notch or two, as it usually does, on the Périphérique around Paris, a section of road that must account for the marital breakdown of thousands of English motorists.

As we neared Calais and left the autoroute it was agreed that the kitten's combined home and litter tray needed some attention, so we pulled in at the next service station. This was the penultimate stopping place ahead of the ferry port and was thronging with returning holidaymakers. By now Charlie's nerves were showing early signs of fraying. She had been chewing her lip, refusing to eat and complaining of an upset stomach since before Paris. I pulled the car up at the edge of the service station car park next to a litterbin and cheerfully set about emptying the cat box, whilst the girls held the kitten. As I was explaining to the girls what a cinch this little caper would be, a small blue van parked up alongside us. I glanced at Charlie as we both read the word Douane written down the side of it. A man in a blue customs uniform got out and leaned on the side of the van in the sunshine and watched intently as we administered to our feline stow-away. I felt a little thumping in chest as the customs officer and I exchanged smiles. Much of the colour had drained out of Charlie's face as we all got back into the car. Had we been rumbled? Was this state surveillance? Were they sending us a message? If 'they' weren't, was God sending one? We sat trying to look casual and waited for the van to leave, as our time for boarding the ferry ticked closer.

As soon as the customs man departed, phase two of the patchy plan commenced. The boot of the car was emptied and the kitten and box were positioned deep within it, surrounded by the ice-blocks. The other contents were then crammed back in and with a little force the lid was closed again. Back on the road, we practised the ventilation protocol. On the command, "armrest down" the girls would reach around together behind their car seats into the middle and pull back the armrest to reveal the plastic ski flap. On the command, "flap up" they would raise the plastic cover to reveal the bars of the cat box and the kitten behind, who would blink and meow. More importantly, we practised the protocol in reverse, with the girls closing the flap and righting the armrest, whereupon the kitten would continue to meow, but in a slightly more muffled way.

As an aside, and as mentioned, the plastic flap separating us and the kitten is described by the ad-men in the aspirational blurb about the car as a ski flap. It is in theory the miniature pull-down hatch through which you can place your skis to rest, after a magical day on the slopes, before effortlessly navigating hairpin bends in an alpine landscape and spending the evening sipping champagne in an outdoor Jacuzzi, with the man or woman of your dreams. We all know the real use of the ski flap is for transporting lengths of 4 by 2 from the DIY superstore, or a rake from the garden centre or something preposterous from IKEA, back to our homes. This day, the ski flap had a more vital use as a cat flap. The little operators in the back seat appeared calm and confident, but the increasingly nervous woman in the passenger seat did not.

French customs and passport control passed smoothly. On the approach to both, I'd turn down the music, gently issue the command words to the minions in the rear seats and watch proudly in the mirror as they efficiently entombed the kitten. The hour and a half car ferry journey had been a worry, and for a moment the prospect of a cat-astrophy loomed as we were directed onto an open deck in the full glare of the early afternoon sun. A distinctly uneasy few minutes passed, with the risk of our car being transformed into an oversized kitten microwave, whilst the sailors shunted the vehicles closer together, drawing us back into the shade. But it was still very hot below decks. To Charlie's annoyance, a group decision was made to leave all the windows open. If you strained your ears a high-pitched meow was audible.

After the tannoy call to re-join our vehicles, it was a race back down to the car deck. The kitten was still peering out of the ski flap and apparently in good shape. Whether it was either very hot from the ambient temperature and confined space or very cold as a result of the ice blocks, it is hard to say.

On rolling off the deck into the sunlight, I gave the "flap down" and "arm rest up" orders, as a lot of high visibility vests and uniforms prowled. We queued towards the self-same mirrored building from my childhood and a slight frisson of anticipation passed over me. It was now my turn to conjure up the innocent calm and conviviality created by my mum on those sunny, by-gone, childhood days when we smuggled contraband across the Channel. This moment was my opportunity to pick up where Mum had left off, by putting the troops at total ease, whilst whisking us all under the mirrored building, past the danger of the customs bays at the other side and on to victory.

Out of the corner of my eye, my peripheral vision suggested that Charlie's thinking was taking her in a somewhat different direction. Her face was an unusual grey and presented a sickly, almost painful grimace. The overall look would have worked well if she had been playing the starring role in a TV hostage drama. Haunted eyes looked out straight into the middle-distance. I reached a hand out onto her knee and said something about how much fun this all was, but it did nothing to stem the sense of crisis that had begun to fill the front of the car and mix with the diesel fumes from the air vents.

Charlotte, with hands shaking, pulled her handbag onto her lap, clutched it as if it was someone dear, then began to search frantically inside. She pulled out a stick of gum, bit on it hard and started to chew on it maniacally. As the mirrored building loomed above us, her breathing became audible, but was punctuated by the whispered mantra of, "Oh God, Oh God, Oh God".

Still moving at a crawl, we emerged back into the sun from the deep shade of the underpass. Ahead lay the covered bays where vehicles were having their contents inspected by customs officials. Before this stood a pair of po-faced officers whose job it was to pull the 'suspicious' cars out of the line and direct them to a vacant bay. In front and to our right, an eager sniffer dog jumped out of a caravan door and, at the direction of its handler, began an excited circuit of the outside. On the other side, stern looking officers with rolled-up sleeves and latex gloves were removing the contents from the boot of a saloon car like ours, as a family looked on from the kerb. I suspected that unlike ours, their boot did not meow. Sat in a trance-like pose next to me, Charlie's respiration was losing depth and gaining pace. Turning her head towards the little girls in the back she let out a faux laugh, which came out more like a shriek and thrust a bag of jelly-tots towards them. The girls looked back quizzically, with a note of alarm, as if weighing up whether to take sweets from a stranger.

Glancing in the rear view mirror, my earlier promise to take the rap if we were caught suddenly seemed braver than intended and I began to wonder if it would be more sensible if our girls, not being of prison age, might do better shouldering the blame? I mean, they wouldn't actually get locked up - would they?

We crawled along through customs, where even the suspicious people who were stuck in the search bays looked suspiciously at us, but soon found ourselves back in multiple lanes of traffic, crossing the perimeter of the port onto the open road. Charlie exhaled a long breath and sighed in relief. I did the same and tried to hide it behind a yawn, but found that the release of tension had left a void that was being filled by paranoia.

Now, only one small phase of the patchy plan was left. We pulled off the road into the town of Dover and headed out to its suburbs. On finding a quiet street of Victorian terraces, we stopped and popped the boot lid. Charlie and I went to the back and furtively unpacked onto the pavement so that the cat box could be liberated from its hiding place. We glanced about, looking for the tell-tale signs of threat; the training CCTV cameras, the plain clothed couple in a parked car, or the person standing at a bus stop with one hand lightly touching an ear. We saw nothing, but surely that's what they wanted us to see? The kitten was placed back between the girls, full of beans, though possibly a little confused. It had been a turbulent few weeks since his birth. He had survived abandonment, a dog attack and trafficking, using up three of his lives in very quick succession. We named him Magic in honour of his early achievements and at our home in Rutland, he grew up to be a prince of cats.

31

It might have been the sense of anti-climax, but for me a mix of melancholy emotions were beginning to take hold as we looked up and down the terraced street at Dover for signs of danger. Parents from all over might recognise this onset of a fugue state. I had wanted to reconstruct part of my childhood, for the benefit of my children, or more likely for myself, but somehow the endeavour had failed. We had, it is true, got away with our little foray into animal trafficking, but it had not been the carefree, celebration of rule breaking that I had expected. Instead, I'd presided over a tense and sweaty experience that had left my children and their kitten baffled and my wife traumatised. Perhaps there is some consolation, as it is likely that I am not the first mum or dad to feel a deep tug of disappointment when trying to recreate the halcyon days of their childhoods for their own families? The enthusiastic urges to re-enact the best of the past are the soft foundations on which a multitude of failed family camping trips, events and excursions are built.

The flaws in my plan had been threefold. The first was to expect that a summer's day of cross-Channel smuggling in 1982 could time travel unharmed to 2011. The second was to attempt to construct cherished memories for my children, which is something that they can only really do for themselves. The third was to expect the same result, but with different ingredients. Charlie is intrinsically good, has a conscience, she draws comfort from a world that is organised by rules and has a healthy respect for authority. Our Calais to Dover trip was never, it turns out, going to be a picnic. As a couple, we had simply been brought up differently and do not share the same view on the rules.

The Lag

By any standards my school was unusual. To conjure a
picture all one has to do is to take Harry Potter's school and
blend it with a corrective institution. Pluck any such
institution from your mind, whether it be a maximum
security penitentiary, a Victorian poorhouse, a debtor's
prison or a dirty-bricked English clink, then overlay with
Hogwarts and voilà.
Established in 1552, with a uniform unchanged since the
same moment, my school had been endowed to save the
waifs and strays of London by Edward the Sixth, the sickly
boy-king and son of the more famous Henry the Eighth.
Today street kids are distant, photographed in the favelas of
South America and the slums and shanti of Africa and
India. But I guess that the jauntily named waifs and strays
of sixteenth century London were every bit as unfortunate
as the modern children who tug at our hearts on charity
advertisements after the news and before our favourite TV.
By good fortune my school had originally been plonked at
Grey Friars in what I imagine once to have been a down-at-
heel district of London, seated between the Tower just to
the east and the Palace of Westminster a little way to the
west. The street kids and slums are long gone and the good
fortune was that Grey Friars is now slap bang in the middle
of the City, Europe's and sometimes the world's money
capital.

300 years on, at the height of the British Empire, the square mile of the City was the very epicentre of about everything that needed financing anywhere on Earth. The school was still there and probably getting in the way. The accumulation of its wealth may have been an incremental selling off one-playing-field-at-a-time affair or perhaps one day a bursar just woke up and thought, "Holy Shit, we're sitting on a goldmine". Either way it was agreed to sell up and move out to a place where the air was cleaner for the poor destitute kids and where, as a happy by-product, the teaching staff could move into an avenue of splendid detached houses. Thus, after the turn of the twentieth century 2,000 or so acres of land were bought in rural Sussex and a model school was built on a vast scale. Girl waifs and strays split to a separate place and moved north finding a home in Hertford.

Effectively our school holds three rings of territory. The huge red brick and limestone quadrangle formed the centre of the inner ring impertinently rivalling anything at Oxford or Cambridge. Around it are clustered stately buildings each ventricles of the heart; the dining hall, the chapel, the science school and the impressively named Royal Mathematical and English Schools flanking the opulently titled Big-School concert hall. In each hung and stood works of art collected over the centuries, some gifted by waifs and strays who'd gone on to better themselves and wanted to prove it.

An avenue of sixteen red bricked and stone mullioned boarding houses each housing sixty inmates intersected the quadrangle, standing like soldiers to attention along the avenue of London plane trees, planted I dare say as a nod to the past. Senior schoolmasters resided on the other side of

34

the road looking out at their charges from panelled rooms.
These and other buildings where lesser subjects were
studied formed the core and included a 200-bed infirmary.
Beyond lay hundreds of acres of playing fields of every
type, with homes for regular teachers between the mown
grass, the pavilions and changing rooms. Copses of trees
were thoughtfully retained to screen one place from another
and to give us boys places to drink and smoke. This was the
middle ring stopping at the gatehouses that marked the
official boundary of the school.

Outside this a generous band of Lebensraum had been
acquired and set aside for, well, who knows what? It was a
buffer circle or insurance policy with tracts of land that
included the school's own railway station, farms and
woods. For its administrators this must have represented
security to the same extent that it amplified a sense of
isolation to the students. Here, dressed in period costumes
we felt every bit as removed as the aspiring wizards of
Hogwarts. Whilst everything that happened in the inner two
rings was either religious or militaristic, the outer ring
provided an area of decompression, so preventing sixteenth
century schoolboys from spooking the locals and the locals
from gawping back. It also seemingly kept any other
authority from prying into the more dubious practices of the
teachers and clergy.

There were three woods accessible to us kids. The
Itchingfield wood of oak, birch and bracken, the bluebell
wood set on a hillside across the railway line and the Lag -
a damp, bad smelling, steep sided valley which was where
much of the real action happened. It was a rundown wood
used by cadets for shooting practice and army exercises and
locals for fly tipping. Drawn to the Lag from the word go,
we made dens there when young and smoked dope there

when a little older. In between, it was there that Bill Hibbs and I tried and failed to blow up a wasp nest with a home-made thermic bomb and where we dragged a couple of abandoned transit van rear doors to sit atop a crater which we had already spanned with timber. The van doors formed part of the roof, which was generously topped with a foot of leaf mould making our hiding place invisible. We smashed the rubber edged window of one, making a trap door into our bunker and used the other as a skylight.

Thrilled by our ingenuity we'd sit triumphantly in the dark on wet clay and smoke lollypop thin rolled cigarettes before getting bored and roaming the woods for something else to salvage and break. If there was nothing to scavenge, we'd visit the concrete shooting wall at the centre of the Lag and poke around for .303 calibre bullet heads buried in the sand at the foot of this huge and peculiar monolith.

By the time I got to the school in 1981 street kids had become hard to find in London. In truth finding 1,200 male, orphan waifs had probably been tricky for a while. So, the waif policy had at some point relaxed a notch making the school a home, proving ground and springboard for deprived inner-city children. However, when it comes to teasing out a subsidised education, the cunning of the middle classes can never be underestimated. I was one of a type that roamed the hallways and filled the classrooms, because I was a fallen middle class boy. True my mum was a single parent from a lowly French family, and true we were at the time of my tenth birthday on our uppers. By that time, I'd also fallen behind at school and taken to mildly delinquent activities with some gusto. But we were not poor or deprived in the real sense of the word. My father, an airline pilot, had left when I was six and had been

36

troublesome and mean in providing maintenance for me and my sister Annabel. But my mum was energetic, loving and diligent at keeping us out of debt whilst she was training to be a teacher. We did not have bad teeth, dropped vowels or the pallor of poverty about us. Because we had a French mum and this was England in the seventies, we ate better than anyone in a ten-mile radius, enjoying sauces that were neither ketchup nor brown, consuming vegetables that weren't peas and eating cheeses that you could not see your reflection in. We were broke, not poor, but then again so were a decent portion of my school friends. A chunk of them had also hit a snake in the class system's game of snakes and ladders. Their families had stumbled, but with a bit of effort and a free top-class education, their children would rise again to buy debentured seats at Lord's cricket ground.

Other kids at school were poor, sporting proper south London accents and fuck-you demeanours. It's no mean feat to carry a truly convincing air of malevolence when wearing knee high felt britches and thigh length yellow socks. The tough kids could though, effortlessly. Thus, being poor was considered cool and kids like me kept quiet about having a well-off dad, or a dad at all and froze in horror if he turned up unexpectedly in a sports car to watch us marching around.

Marching around was what we mostly did, starting at 7.15 every morning before breakfast. We marched on Wednesdays and Saturdays before lunch and those who got a kick from it marched in their spare time too, by joining the Combined Cadet Force. Others who were far sighted enough to see the opportunities, joined the 150 strong marching band which did ceremonial stuff at national occasions and major sporting events. Others threw themselves into sport itself chasing a place in the first eleven or fifteen. That left two categories, the nerds and the 'none-of-the-above'. The nerds suffered for their nerdery. A nerd with grit might survive and even thrive, but one without was destined to a spirit crushing eight years of schooling. The none-of-the-abovers by contrast were not necessarily an unhappy bunch. Being lazy and feckless takes a certain resolve and energy. It also creates its own range of shared experiences and bonhomie, though perhaps not the character-building ones that were advertised on the school prospectus. What's more, the same kind of street-wise that allows you to shirk beneath the adults' radar also enables a kid to anticipate and avoid a direct hit from a 'shit shuttlecock' launched by Tom Cotter over the partition of the next-door toilet cubicle. Like career criminals, we malingerers knew the score and were nobody's fools.

As boys who generally fell into the 'none-of-the-above' category, we drifted into a senior house that carried the name of a literary figure who'd attended in the eighteenth century. By reputation, my institution-within-an-institution had a tradition of being liberal, but low achieving. Our housemaster was a dapper, blonde and bearded English teacher, who cared a great deal for the arts, but very little about what time we went to bed. If our socks were down or our coats missed buttons, it was up to his younger deputy to enforce standards, but even with a background as a South African army PT instructor, he failed at most attempts to convert us into anything less slouched and ragged. Aside from a contemporary who went on to captain industry and one who advised a British prime minister, we were destined to mediocrity at best. The tough kids sometimes left at sixteen having already outgrown their surroundings to start jobs or to apply their elevated numeracy toward the distribution of narcotics.

On Wednesday and Saturday when the other, better versions of us were out performing in the band or striving on sports fields, we would doss. Even today dossing (whether they know it or not) is the chosen pastime of bored adolescent boys when they lack the privacy to play with themselves. We'd laze about on doss-beds made from spare hand-me-down mattresses and smelly beanbags, listening to music and punctuating our long afternoons with trips out to smoke skinny cigarettes behind buildings. From memory, this and occasionally successful attempts to brew beer in buckets and then decant it into exploding plastic milk bottles took most of our time. The rest was spent in the age-old pursuit of insulting each other's mothers whereby the answer to any quip would simply be, "Yer mum". The required reply would be, "Well yer mum's on the game," inviting the response, "Yeah, yer mum does it for biscuits - that's why she's so fat". These were just the stock warm-up rounds. We would spend our afternoons thus in groups of three or four. But even amongst malingerers there is often a need for something more social.

On a Wednesday lunchtime in the din of the packed dining hall, as other boys made plans for set-piece moves on the rugby field, a question might be asked about a mud-fight in the Lag. Neither the season nor the weather outside would determine when, but if the zeitgeist was about right and the preceding weather had been wet, a few heads might nod and quiet conversations would ensue at the tables on either side. A mud-fight was not to be broadcast. It was neither a noble nor cool pursuit for kids aged fourteen to eighteen who prided themselves on a hard won image of wasting afternoons listening to The Clash and The Doors. It was also a minor house ritual of our own making that did not require the attentions of like-minded interlopers or adult teachers. Loose arrangements would be made to meet at an agreed time in the house changing room, where we'd change into whatever sports kit we owned, or could requisition from the pegs of absent sportsmen. Then, we the misfits in our mismatched sports clothes, some wearing other people's plimsoles, would wander out towards the Lag leaving an entire boarding house to two or three grateful nerds.

Layabouts don't travel en masse, so we'd arrive at the shooting wall of the Lag in dribs and drabs via different routes, like tribesmen gathering for a ceremony. When roughly quorate we'd divide into two teams of equal number with around ten to twelve boys each. The defending group, the one that had elected to defend the wall, would take up positions around it. The attacking group would climb back up to the valley's opposing edge looking back down at the meandering stream and start discussing strategies on how we might best 'take the wall'. Staring down through the canopy at the twenty-foot-high shooting wall from the firing positions of the school's cadets, the defenders in their brightly striped rugby shirts and borrowed cricket whites looked like tropical fish in a barrel. Meanwhile the defenders would be considering their own advantages, the first being the bottleneck created by the narrow bridge of just six railway sleepers that crossed the brook and the second being the half acre of bog on the opposite side of the stream at the very floor of the valley, before the steep sandy rise to the foot of the wall itself.

Soon the game would be afoot and without rules or referee it would be anyone's guess on how things would play out. The little fleet-of-foot sneaky guy in me would push out wide when attacking, taking an elaborate root down the valley side and jumping the stream at a meander onto a gravel beachlet. I'd decide against traversing the sewage pipe that crossed the stream at chest height, knowing that it was too good an ambush point for defenders to pancake a guy and send him into the water below. So furtively I'd attempt to outflank the opposition, moving from tree to tree up the other side of the valley, until at the same altitude as the wall. Once there, I'd be poised to come and claim it by stealth. Meanwhile, others were deploying more confrontational tactics, with Frank Redmond, a boy with questionable IQ coupled with an inability to calculate risk, charging down to the open boggy area, slopping at-a-pace through it and then crouching shin deep as if tending a paddy field to scoop up goo. By this time defenders would be lobbing large pats of mud in arcs from higher ground that would land with a loud plop and a spray of mud-grit shrapnel. This was not just mud, it was virgin mud of a texture used for beauty products, but with the stench of decay about it. It was more cow shit than face mask. A hapless attacker like Frank might arrive at the little bridge as if he'd received a broadside from a muck spreader. At this point, straining with blurred mud vision and unbalanced by the unusual ankle weight, he'd be up-ended into the water and carried away by the current downstream past the stands of giant hogweed and wild garlic. This act of selfless stupidity and the ensuing laughter would allow two or three others to slurp through the bog to the stream edge and consider options, whilst crouching to lift mud. But, by then Dan 'Benny' Brinton and Dave Gill, both lanky lads with good throwing arms had jumped down a tier from the foot of the wall to unleash mud volleys of a sufficient velocity to decapitate. Since the projectiles were merely slurry mixed with grit, they simply enrobed a moving target with a slap turning it grey. This happened to the accompaniment of Dave screaming his "Eat shit motherfuckaaa" battle cry, delivered incongruously in the strained voice of Jacob Rees-Mogg.

With the defenders' midfield players now on the attack, we opportunists had our chance. But by now the pointless objective of capturing a concrete wall had been replaced by mud-lust. Seizing clods of mud from our adversaries' stores, the scouts behind enemy lines made our break in unison delivering cowardly back-of-the-bonce blows to the defenders. In the growing tumult, a big strong lump like Elvis Williams would finally lumber at full tilt across the bridge before squelching ankle deep into the bog beyond, flailing like an exhausted prize fighter whilst receiving a caking. At this stage recognising who was who was tricky. The mud travelled in every direction and those at the centre of it were already a swampy, blackened grey. In desperation the last attackers would eschew the bridge and launch themselves waist deep into the stream. Equally desperate defenders dropped armfuls of mud headward at point blank range, before being tackled at the knees and falling backwards into their bog. Like feeding fish drawn to a baited area, the rancid smell of virgin mud, combined with disturbed pockets of methane and crushed wild garlic drove us on into frenzy. Smaller boys were trodden into the mud where they lay. Bigger guys were set upon and rolled down the bank sidelong into the stream. Whoops, yelps, shouts, profanities and mud filled the air. It wasn't medieval, it was pre-historic. It was one part danger and three parts stupidity. It was truly, marvellous fun.

After a couple more minutes of mud and mayhem things would calm. Someone would get hurt and the intensity would die. There would be a pause to go looking for lost shoes and even socks and the swapping of war stories, whilst the odd contact lens would be removed and jettisoned. As all were by now plastered in mud from head to toe and many were already soaked, one by one we would drop into the stream to drift under the bridge, holding on at the far edge to leave a plume of grey-brown as the current rinsed mud from our clothes, hair and skin. Then, in single file as one group we would swim, wade and splash along the stream to the outer limits of the Lag, where the valley ended abruptly as if blocked by a landslide. This is where it had been filled in for the rail line to cross. Here, the meandering stream had been channelled into a small, long, black tunnel. By our tradition, traversing the tunnel was the last rite of passage for the day. On entering, crouched and apprehensive, the light at the end appeared small indeed. Cobwebs and obstructions caused shrieks and the swearing echoed into the deep. Most of the whispered subterranean talk was of strange creatures capable of gnashing at testicles, but what else would boys talk about during such sublime moments as our self-made adventure came to a close?

Quite early on, just as kids reach adolescence, we are assigned future roles in life. There are the all-rounders who are sporting heroes as well as being academically gifted. They will naturally go on to master the universe and become our leaders. If just sporty or bright you are on track

43

to being a solid professional type. And it's known begrudgingly that the nerds will inherit the Earth by shaping our world through science and technology or another less likely obsession. For the rest of us, the average or poor achievers, the drop-outs and the troublemakers who reside in the 'none of the above category' our trajectory is to mediocrity. Nothing great is expected.

But returning back on the long walk from the Lag on those occasional Wednesday afternoons, caked in filth, leaving puddles on the asphalt where we trod, we 'the mediocre' were the victors. On these days, those of us that had been left behind were masters of our own time and captains of our imaginations. Though shivering and wet, we were glorying in our teenaged years, unsupervised and released from the ways of a sports field or the adult world beyond. Together we could make our own rules and we were brothers in mud.

To No Man But The King

I only recall meeting Charlotte's grandfather on three occasions. His name was Peter Kirkby. The last time I saw him was when we visited him at his ground floor room in an old people's home outside Leicester. It was a bright spring morning following rain. We looked out from the floral curtains onto his neat little terrace and at the birdfeeder that hung from a tree beyond. He stooped a bit more than I had remembered and his fine bushy eyebrows drooped a little more heavily on his brow, but he was still a tall, softly spoken, elegant man with kind eyes. Not surprisingly, Peter had become something of a favourite with the women residents of the home and we all joked about his attentions being in unquenchable local demand from the female inmates.

At his funeral, his eldest daughter Vaccy, my mother-in-law, read out a short story that he had sent to her two months before he died. Ever since, I have held onto it in my mind. There is nothing sensational about the prose or in fact the story itself, but there is lingering poignancy that gives it a delicate gravitas. It comes from a time and place and from a type of person that many of us will have met only once or twice in our lives. Peter was a modest gentleman, of a type who existed before everyone became so brash and so brazen.

He called it 'To no man but the King' and it goes like this:

My father's rule on Sunday mornings was to take notice of the early weather forecast and from that decide whether he should take the dogs for their five mile walk in the morning or afternoon.

On the day in mind, he had decided to go soon after breakfast and, as usual, I went with him, I wearing the cap of my new school at which I was due to start the next morning. I was ten years old, but not used to wearing a cap and not well acquainted with the finer courtesies required by this.

We had not been far along the lane from Drayton to Costessey before we met the Hon. Finch J.P. from Costessey New Hall. The two men exchanged greetings by raising their walking sticks and I put up what might be described as a two finger 'cub salute'. When the men had finished expressing their opinion of the weather and general condition of the dogs, up went their walking sticks, up went my 'cub salute', and we went our separate ways. When we were out of ear-shot, my father said, "You should have raised your cap to Mr. Finch". I replied that he hadn't, so I did the same as he. He said, "Well, I can't fault you for following my example, but what I am saying now is that it is different for you and me. You are a boy and whilst you are a boy you should raise your cap to another gentleman, and I stress gentleman, as a courtesy. I am a man and can please myself what I do and since I have been a man, whilst always doing so to ladies, I raise my hat to no man but the King".

We went on our way, I thinking of whom we might meet and how I would decide who was entitled to a raised cap and who could be passed off with a cub salute. We called in at the Rose and Crown in Costessey where I had a ginger pop in the garden and solved the hat problem for the return journey by putting my cap in my pocket.

I was reminded of this event some twelve years later. I was in Norwich on the first of fourteen days' leave following the birth of our first daughter and was walking from the nursing home along the railings bounding the Norfolk and Norwich Hospital. There was practically no traffic on the road and very few pedestrians as everyone employable had been directed into work for the war effort.

As I approached the hospital gate, where the carriageway crossed the pavement, I noticed a Police Commissioner and Sergeant standing in the road looking up the driveway to the hospital entrance and as I neared the gate the Sergeant walked forward and signalled me to stop. Glancing up the drive I saw a very smart car with a standard flying - a VIP of some sort who would justify a salute. As the car came slowly through the narrow gate, I took a sideways squint and wow! the King! As the car slowly nosed its way through the narrow gate, I saw King George VI, in Naval uniform, sitting on my side of the back seat. Up went what I hope was the smartest salute in all England that day and in response I received a personal salute as there were no others anywhere near me.

As the car turned to go into the city, the Police Sergeant signalled me on. I went on my way feeling very pleased with myself - it was the first of fourteen days' leave and not only had I found my wife, contrary to my expectations, blooming like a June rose, I had a beautiful baby daughter and a Royal Salutation to mark the event. I thought what a pity the old man could not have been with me, so that just for once, I could have done the saluting and he could have raised his hat to the King.

Peter Kirkby
June 2003

There are two addenda to this story. The first is that the baby daughter in question, born in Grove House Maternity Home, Norwich in 1942, was Vaccy. For the second, we have to go back to the nursing home in Leicestershire. Ever the fidget, I moved about the small room looking at the artefacts on the walls and the curios on the shelves, before my eyes rested on a small framed medal. Looking closely, I could read that it was a Distinguished Flying Cross, a medal for 'exemplary gallantry in active operations against the enemy in the air'.

The family knowledge of Peter's war is only partial. It transpires that Peter was radio operator on Wellington bombers during World War II. By fate, or by luck, he completed two full operational tours flying at night over enemy occupied Europe.
Bomber Command had the highest death toll amongst our armed forces during the war, losing sixty per cent of its operational servicemen. During this time, he survived two plane crashes, before being transferred to Air Sea Rescue on Walruses. By then and as with a large number of his comrades, his nerves were beginning to fray. I know this by inference only. After the end of hostilities, he went back to

48

a quiet civilian life as a nurseryman and seed salesman, still occasionally haunted by the War. Vaccy recalls, as a young child, being woken from her sleep and carried by her father, through to the inner hallway of their flat, where the family would all shelter and wait out a thunderstorm. Fear of thunderstorms and of fire were the natural results of surviving the maelstrom anti-aircraft fire and of being trapped in a burning aircraft after it crashed. Today we would call it post-traumatic stress disorder, or PTSD.

I enquired about the medal in the frame. Peter confirmed that it was a DFC and said, with a modest pride, that he had received it at Buckingham Palace from King George VI himself. I asked him if he and the King had spoken at all during the ceremony. He said that they had, so I pushed on a little further and asked what they had discussed. He responded that, though the exchange had been nothing of great importance, he had never told anyone about it, because what was said was,
"Between me and my King".

History is Written...

Fifteen years ago, I did a stint in nature conservation, working for a government agency whose job it was to protect dumb animals from the even dumber species that have mastery over them. We needed to punch above our weight in all things to get anything of significance done. A little mantra had developed to underpin our modus operandi; 'History is made by those who turn up' signified to our staff, that putting in the extra mile was necessary, if we were to in any way soften the ravages of humanity and its spiralling free-market economies. In practice, this meant tacking on an extra meeting to a busy day in London, or staying for an early evening event, because the only way to influence important decisions was to be there. Similarly, the way to get your points into a critical document, was to offer to write it. The results were good, in fact so good, that it was rumoured that the Treasury Department found us such an irritant, that it put out a government wide fatwa against us and began plotting our demise. There, I got into the habit of writing stuff down and have been occasionally writing stuff down ever since.

I implored my dad to do the same, because unlike me, he had a ready reserve of really good stuff with which to enthral a reader - all drawn from a colourful life. In fact, his stories were so good that from a young age, I began to remember them and tell them to other people. Many were inappropriate, particularly when handed down by father to son, as they regularly contained in-passing references to sexual conquests whilst he was 'down-route', but still married to my mum. So engaging were they that sometime after, friends would ask me to recount my third party stories whilst we were seated in bars or rambling at the end of a dinner party. Dad had been a very young co-pilot and then jet-plane captain during the golden age of civil aviation, when the skies were clear and spanned a seemingly unencumbered world, which still remained to be explored. He'd revelled in the freedom given to a young man who was working a dream job in a near dream world. It was the grey-brown era of the late sixties and seventies where a malaise of strikes and piles of rubbish tainted our own island, but by contrast, his life was one of practical jokes, of exotic place names and most of all of the unadulterated pleasures of sun, sea, booze and sex.

To me as a very small child, he seemed never there, but then just to appear from the bedroom, bleary-eyed and lighting a fag, after catching up on some sleep. Or he might just stride down the garden path in the middle of a summer afternoon, his captain's cap worn at a non-regulation angle, whilst my sister and I were having our tea. He might come home with the bruises sustained from falling from a rum boat in Barbados, or with a whole ham flung over his shoulder after a short hop to Cologne. Nothing was ever certain. What was certain, was that at some place or other around the world it would be nearing six o'clock, so a drink would never be very far off, no matter which time zone Dad found himself in.

I reckon that I was only five, possibly six, when one early morning I awoke to find my father crouched in my bedroom, his grinning face bathed in light as it peered between a crack in the curtains out on to the opposite side of the Close. His quarry was our neighbour Dave. Dave was a printer who had left the grime of Fleet Street newspaper printing to raise a family and to enjoy village cricket in Sussex. He would leave in the early morning to run his nearby printing presses in Horsham. As he left home this particular morning, things had not started well for Dave. Because today, as he had absentmindedly pulled the choke out then turned the key, the engine had spluttered momentarily before it caught, but when he instinctively pressed down on his right foot, a screechy high-pitched whine accompanied the revving. So shrill was it that Dave shot a hand forward to extinguish the engine. He sat for a second, then tried the same operation again, but this time more purposefully, starting the engine carefully with just a nudge on the accelerator. The car ticked over quietly as Dave listened. All appeared well, save for a slightly unusual hum, so he set the machine into reverse and applied the accelerator again. A second gaspy shriek broke the early morning calm of Needles Close. It was coming from the car alright, but where exactly was hard to identify. As Dad giggled in elation from behind my curtains across the road, the bonnet shuddered under the tension of its own release. Walking to the front, Dave peered in and tugged hopefully at the fan belt as the engine idled. Wearing a troubled expression and muttering, he reset the bonnet, returned to the wheel and reattempted the same operation. At low revs the car crept backward, with the strange new sound raising in timbre. Alarmed by the cause and effect of foot extension to increase in volume and pitch, he took the car

53

out of gear and once again tried the accelerator. Slowly as he depressed, the hum rose, before reaching a tipping point and switching to another alarming squeal, breaking the early morning silence for a third time. Muttering the mantra, "bloody car" to himself, Dave got out once again and circled it like a predator. It purred gently back in defiance. Another poke at the accelerator with the driver's door open sent my Dad into near delirium. This time a red-faced man of intent arose from the car. With the engine ruled out as the culprit, he crouched and then lent with one hand on the ground as he peered underneath it. With nothing amiss, he worked his way along the underside of the car and around to the boot lid. Coming face-to-face with the exhaust pipe, he first squinted, then poked a finger at the pipe's rim as it puffed and gave up the odd drip of water. Then with two fingers and thumb, he tugged at an alien object, pulling it free. The Muffler Whistle™, bought by my dad somewhere stateside was now in his hand. Without hesitation, Dave turned toward our home and as my father ducked from view, he launched it at the house, before getting into the car, slamming the door and disappearing at speed.

This little prank was something of an aberration. Most seemed to happen when Dad was meant to be at work, either as a pilot actually in the driver's seat of an aeroplane, or as the captain and figurehead of a crew that were resting 'down-route'. In those days, the flight deck and cabin crew of charter airlines sometimes went on holiday with their passengers. If on a long haul trip, they would oftentimes fly their passengers out, reside in the same hotels, or better ones, share the same sunshine and mirth, before sobering up just enough to get them back up to 37,000 feet again and

54

take them home. Whilst short haul flying still entailed some
nasty and long shifts, a trip to the Caribbean in those days
might take ten days out of a busy captain's roster. As today,
the cheapest landing slots at the airports are either early or
late, so Mum would occasionally wake us, lead a pair of
bleary-eyed munchkins to the car, where she had already
put the back seats down and spread out blankets. From our
nest, I'd stare up at the sodium lights as we approached
Gatwick to pick up Dad. If the aeroplane was returning in
the daylight, we would sometimes drive down a bumpy
track that stopped at a padlocked gate, where the
countryside ended and the airport started. There we would
wait, sometimes for quite a while, for the aeroplane to land.
Mum would then put us back in the car and drive us around
to the office. If the aeroplane happened to taxi all the way
to the hangar, she tells me that we would sometimes be let
through and drive almost right up to it. However the
collection happened, he'd be washed out and jet-lagged and
handsome, but I think I remember that he was always
excited to see us, even if by the next evening he was
straight out at 6.30 to the pub.

By the late seventies, and as a forerunner to the ubiquitous
low-cost airlines of the twenty first century, Dad was flying
the Skytrain to New York. Flying to New York had once
been the preserve of the rich. Starting at £59 per passenger,
this service on the new DC 10 passenger jet made
transatlantic travel accessible to a whole new audience. As
a result, the airline and its employees soon gained immense
public affection. The crews also sensed that they were onto
something a bit different. From the moment the seatbelt
signs were extinguished after take-off, a procession of
passengers would visit the cockpit to 'ooh' and 'aah' at the

hundreds of instruments crammed into the tiny space. I guess that Dad would have been his charming and disarming self to what he called the 'what-a-lot-of-clocks-brigade'. For me, I part imagine and part remember that time a little dimly, in the slightly grainy tone of a stylish seventies' movie.

Landing at JFK, the flight deck and the cabin crew, all dressed in uniforms created by a famous fashion designer, would be swooshed into Manhattan in two long limousines, which would draw up alongside stylish, modern hotels sporting names like Hilton, Sheraton or Intercontinental. The air hostesses, who had been hand-picked in beauty contests, would turn heads in the lobby as they checked-in. Despite being weary from twelve hours at work, the majority of the crew would ready themselves for a night out in the city that never sleeps.

Before disembarking the crew from a flight, the captain of an airliner signs a flurry of paperwork which is presented to him on a small clipboard. The triplicate sheets are manifests, fuel and weight loads and suchlike, but also contain a summary of the bar and duty-free cash-take on the flight. If the chief flight attendant or bursar had flown with my father before and knew his M.O., they would play out the little straight-faced ritual of pointing to a hand written footnote, explaining that a bottle of vodka and occasionally a bottle of gin too had been broken on landing. Dad would initial the box and a member of the crew would clank off the aircraft with a duty-free bag in hand. On the ride into town, someone would offer up their room as venue for the crew party, so that a swift session of preloading of vodka and G&T could occur before descending to the hotel bar for a swiftie and then wandering out into either the balmy throng of a New York summer or its icy winter chill. Like all good parties, the following morning the crew would congregate over a very leisurely hotel breakfast and slowly piece together the action of the night before.

Occasionally Annabel and I would be party to the recounting of a story between Dad and Mum, such as the return to the hotel in a yellow cab of a diminutive, impeccably dressed, but exceptionally camp senior cabin steward. He had paid his fare in the shelter of the hotel's canopy, but before reaching the revolving doors the New York cabbie yelled out,

"*Hey fairy*, you've forgotten your wand!"

The hotel's two doormen bit down on a grin as the steward paused, but then turned and glared theatrically, before mince-marching back down the steps to retrieve his umbrella from the backseat. Back on the sidewalk, with his arm at full extension, he then circled the umbrella around the perplexed cabbie's face,

"In that case… I'll turn you into shit," exclaimed the steward, before tossing his head up in triumph and marching back up to the revolving door.

Professional life had not always been so effervescent for my father. After training on Tiger Moths in Perth, Scotland, he landed his first job flying the daily newspapers out pre-dawn, from Southend to Jersey each morning. The aeroplane in question, the lumbering Bristol Freighter, had a huge opening nose cone that could take bigger bits of freight including cars, meaning that the tiny and cold cockpit could only be accessed by propping a ladder against it and clambering up. The airline was called Channel Air Bridge and was the second successful flying venture of an older, more seasoned aviator called Freddie Laker. Laker went on to become a famous airline entrepreneur and one of Britain's most flamboyant businessmen. Next, Dad took a job as a first officer for Aer Lingus in Dublin, where my Mum had arrived only months before, first as an au-pair from deepest rural France, then as a translator, before becoming an air hostess.

The setting up of a 'this & that' airline called Laker Airways brought them to Sussex. To describe the earliest incarnation of Laker as an 'Airways' is to overstate somewhat its capabilities. Dad generally flew whatever aeroplane he was told to, with whatever contents that were on board, human or otherwise, to wherever there was a profit to be made. If Trotters Independent Traders had ever gone airborne, it would have found a direct competitor in the early Laker Airways business. The aircraft were a mixed bag too, from wartime DC9 Dakotas, to the more modern, four propellered Britannia passenger plane. The firm's base was a suite of sparse offices along the old Gatwick airport perimeter with a single hanger that could be mistaken for a large agricultural building. Manning the phone in the Ops room was a chain-smoking, bomber command veteran by the name of Atty Atkinson. Atty had played a small role in bombing Berlin flat in the war, whereas his younger boss Freddie had ironically made his first fortune during the Berlin Airlift of the Cold War. For Freddie and Atty, Dad was their Rodney, a twenty-six-year-old rooky pilot that they could send anywhere to do almost anything. They loved him like a kid brother for it.

In the early days, Dad and his crew would depart from Gatwick, often with air freight, to somewhere sticky and hot with an exotic name. If the ailing aircraft went sick, he would divert to somewhere even stickier and set down. Then the captain would pull out the wad of notes in pounds

58

and dollars that had been stuffed in his pocket for such an eventuality and scout about the tarmac for someone who might fix the aeroplane. The fixing might take a few hours or occasionally days. After setting up the repair, the next duty was to inform Atty in the Ops room at Gatwick. This involved finding someone at the airport with a telex machine and through either charm or hard currency getting a telex sent - to a bookmakers in Horley in Sussex. Laker Airways did not own a telex machine. After reading the racing form over a couple of lunchtime libations at the Aeroclub near Gatwick, Atty would pop into the bookmakers and whilst there he would discover the whereabouts of his aeroplane and its crew. Once fixed, Dad would sometimes be sent to pay cash for a full tank of aviation fuel, then back to work they'd go.

All the work didn't happen under the baking sun though. Transatlantic flying also came into the mix, but the aircraft were not always advanced enough to make it across the Atlantic in just a few hours and without refuelling. Just this month Qantas has trialled a London to Sydney non-stop flight. This twenty-plus-hours long haul flight-a-thon is a world away from the twenty-eight days it once took to fly from London to Sydney in the very early days of civil aviation. Even decades later in the very early seventies, a flight to the USA might involve a refuelling stop at Shannon on the Irish Atlantic or somewhere like Newfoundland off the outer eastern edge of Canada. Flights in general were more likely to be diverted in those days, due to technical issues or bad weather. I think that it was to Halifax airport in Canada that one of his flights was diverted and where the crew were put up in a motel as heavy snow fell across the eastern seaboard. Early in the dark of the next morning, twelve inches of overnight snow had been ploughed from Halifax's runway. Soon after, as a late dawn broke, a blower was also banking up the motel carpark snow. Most of the crew had clambered onto the transport minibus by the appointed time, but it was soon noticed that the nervous (and likely to be unusually hungover) first officer was not aboard and a glance across to his motel room showed that the curtains were still closed. Dad considered the situation for a second and then put two opposing activities into play. The first was to ask a member of the crew to pop back into the hotel to request that the receptionist make a second wake-up call to the darkened room and the other was to stroll over to the snow blower and to tap on the window of the cab. A short, friendly conversation ensued and a ten-dollar bill was passed from one hand to another. Meanwhile lights had come on in the room and the curtains had twitched. Inside, after a few seconds with both hands on the temples and a few more of re-orientation, the first officer had sprung into panicked action. With the churning and thudding of a nearby snowblower as the soundtrack, he sped to the bathroom, pulled on his uniform and shoes and stuffed everything that remained into a case before drawing a breath, grabbing his two bags and heading for the door, turning the handle and pulling it open. By now, the crew bus had been moved, so that events could be observed more discretely and from an optimum angle. As it was only just the very top of the door that was now visible behind a small mountain of snow, its opening had greater impact from the inside where the dulled senses of the first officer were presented by a pearlescent wall of white that was sheer, save for the imprint of a door in it. Somewhat freaked out by the morning's chain of events, he peered in horror into the daylight on tiptoes, to see his crew bus, apparently at the

60

point of leaving for the airport. On the bus, the crew looked back with great interest as the top section of the motel room's window slid downward and two cases and a pilot's cap were ejected to a quiet thud on the path. They however broke into raucous applause, as their backlit first officer stood first on a chair and from it onto the sill where, without pause he tumbled, knee and shoulder first, over the window frame into twelve inches of white powder. He dragged himself to his feet, his hangover now cured, gathered his belongings and boarded the bus to a standing ovation.

Laker Airways was on the way to becoming a proper airline by the early seventies, but as with most talented businessmen, Freddie Laker remained a canny opportunist. When things went wrong for us Brits in Rhodesia, Dad was sent to Dar es Salaam with the Britannia under orders to wait, ahead of the anticipated evacuation of white people from the country. But on seeing on the TV that many white farmers were going to stay, Freddie changed tack. A message was sent to strip the big aeroplane back to its fuselage and board it with plywood. Dad, his co-pilot and engineer rustled-up some local labour and began the task of removing the many dozens of seats and the other accoutrements of a passenger aeroplane. He was then instructed to find an empty oil barrel and to use it to calculate how many such barrels the aeroplane could hold, so that Freddie could work out the most profitable balance of cargo (kerosene, fuel oil, dried foods, luxuries and ammunition) the plane could transport in for the embattled farmers.

With time to spare and instructions from base to cram as much into the aircraft as possible, Dad decided to dismantle the toilets. The Britannia was quite a machine and was a very well-appointed airliner, with fixtures that harked back to the golden age. As such, it had a gents' and ladies' toilet compartment with even urinals for the former. By now the operation to strip the aeroplane had left the three crew members filthy. Despite the help of local labour, their uniforms were soiled and stained. After staggering down the steps in 35° heat with a porcelain urinal and lugging it across the baking tarmac, Dad paused to wipe sweat from his eyes with his shirt sleeves and adjusted his captain's cap into the heat haze to better see a crowd of oncoming people. The British Airways flight from Heathrow to Tanzania had just arrived and its passengers were making the trip across to the arrivals hall. With no choice other than to wait patiently and tip his cap to the line of business people and holidaymakers, Dad watched as their eyes moved up to the Laker Airways airliner, then down to its filthy sweat-stained captain, who appeared to be cuddling a urinal on the tarmac. At the end of the procession came a gaggle of hostesses followed by the two BA pilots and flight engineer, all walking tall in full uniform with their pilot's cases. They stared in abject disgust. But as BA pulled fleeing people from the Rhodesian crisis, the disgraceful dirt-stained men seen in Dar es Salaam that day, were cleaning up, by flying badly needed supplies back in. Laker continued to send his young protégé on missions across Eastern and Southern Africa. Dad remarked that he and his crew would get a sense of how kosher the cargo was, by the speed of the unloading. Medicines might be left for a while to warm in the cargo bay, but when it came to guns, a large reception party would be waiting for the engines to silence, before emptying the hold in a matter of

62

minutes. One day Mum got a call from Atty in the Ops room. It was one of those calls that began with the phrase, "Now there's nothing to worry about, but…".
Dad was under house arrest and the aeroplane had been impounded for gun running.
"He might be a few days late in getting home," was Atty's conclusion. At the time Uganda was warring with Tanzania, but Mum can't remember if he was held by the Ugandans or the Tanzanians, remarking that he could have been flying for either side, quite possibly both.

The resupply of Rhodesian stay-behinds was dwarfed when Freddie Laker began to pioneer The Hajj market, now described as, 'the largest mass gathering in the world'. In the early seventies, it was the arrival of new wide-bodied jets with easier leasing arrangements that provided the raw materials to meet the unseen opportunity of enabling Muslims to make their obligatory pilgrimage to Mecca and satisfy the fifth and final pillar of Islam. By now, Laker Airways was flying half a million tourists to the Canary and Balearic Islands in the spring and summer. In the mid and late seventies, Hajj dates were in the November and December months, a time of year where both charter and scheduled airlines did everything that they could to staunch the haemorrhaging of their summer profits. Winter was the lean period that a holiday airline needed to just get through to survive. Again Laker, soon to be Sir Freddie, sniffed the opportunity of using the winter season to put on charter flights from all over the Indian sub-continent, Africa and elsewhere, thereby enabling many hundreds of thousands of Muslims to visit Mecca.
Laker Airways' youngest captain was again in on the action flying the Boeing 707, which in aviation terms was the

muscle car of the skies. My memories of Dad's personal accounts of the Hajj are a bit vague. They mingle with the other stories and myths that circulated the airline from that time. There was talk over the years of flights to the most remote corners of the Muslim world in North and Central Africa, where the men boarding the aircraft had barely even seen one before. So, it's not surprising that many aspects of jet travel were unfathomable. Thus, the stories were about the attempted lighting of fires to cook food, by the passengers, whilst in the cruise, or a failure to understand the operation of the toilets, or even that defecating required a toilet at all. A small complement of air stewardesses often numbering just two would be on duty. They might be reduced to simple crowd control, before retreating into the cockpit for the bulk of the flight. In between flights, the aircraft required fumigation and at the end of the season the interiors were stripped. So go the stories about the flying latrines of snot and sputum that would arrive in Mecca from some of the least developed places on the Hajj.

I do remember Dad mentioning the problem with Zamzam water. This water is drawn from a holy well at Mecca and when Muslims do the Hajj, it is normal to drink Zamzam water and to bring some back home to share amongst friends and family. Back in the seventies, many pilgrims would bring large metal cans of water home from the holy well. As with modern day flying, the weight of the aeroplane is always a problem, so pilgrims would routinely be told that their attempts to repatriate Zamzam water had been overambitious and that the large can could not be brought on board. It is normal for the captain of an aeroplane to do a visual inspection after boarding, but in those Hajj days it was essential. When all were aboard, Dad would have a quick walk around the hot apron to remove any cans of Zamzam water that had been hopefully placed in the undercarriage bay or in the jet engine intakes.

It seemed that one day we would be talking about his favourite burger joint at Macy's in New York, where a melt-in-the-mouth cheeseburger would accompany a late morning Bloody Mary, or how he had manhandled a preposterously big piece of garden equipment back from Costco in Miami. Then somehow the next time, we would be on the phone discussing the weight of cat litter, the time taken queueing for a prescription, or I'd be getting a full account of his weekly shopping trip to Tesco. It'll probably happen to most of us and is already happening here, as the pressures of ill-health force me to shrink too. My fearful mind scouts around this morose kind of territory too often and I wonder if on his retirement, George, that's my father, left a piece of his identity somewhere at high altitude? By his last trip at Virgin Atlantic, he had joined the ranks of company executives who - as per the celebrity chefs named Jamie or Delia, Nigella or Gordon - only required a christian name. Though no longer in the left-hand driver's seat and having lost the title of fleet captain years before, Dad had still picked the crew for his final flight, which was naturally a trip to New York.

At JFK, the evening scramble by the competing airline pilots to get the wheels off and secure a place in the pecking order to deliver the fastest route home had not gone well, so it was a mild surprise on moving to Heathrow's beacon the next morning that the Virgin 747 was cleared for immediate descent and not instructed to tour London's skyline in the stack. However, on landing the flight deck's hope of getting onto the M25 before the morning rush hour were dashed, as the control tower gave them a place on the outer stand and not a number for one of the main terminal's jetways. Then a lengthy taxi around the perimeter brought an unusual sight. Along with a small line of buses queueing next to a cluster of baggage tractors, Heathrow's fire trucks flanked the passage ahead in salute, issuing plumes of water from their cannons, for the massive airliner to travel through. The passengers were disembarked and memento photos were taken, before the crew were driven to the terminal, where the airline's well known owner was there with his trademark grin, to greet Dad for a surprise retirement party. That the party started at 8am was fitting for a man who had spent the previous forty-five years straddling scrambled time zones and who, even when at home, might choose to have breakfast for lunch and dinner in the early hours of the morning.

As my Dad's star faded his health shrank back. First painful gout, that put painful haemorrhoids and dodgy bowels into the shade. These were ailments for us to chuckle about, but then came alarming, undiagnosed seizures, followed by cancer and then by cancers. He aged suddenly and his skin thinned and freckled. In the tropics, the sun sets quickly. So it was for Dad. True, he had not made longevity a serious life goal, but the decline was shocking all the same, because despite the constant thrashing, he had kept a touch of Peter Pan for so long.

His wealth of exotic stories from Europe, the Middle East, the Orient, Australia, Africa and the USA went with him. Some were blue, others poignant, others bathed in the accidental geo-politics or social history of the moment. Occasionally, I travelled along for the ride too, as a kid and an adult. One sultry afternoon in 1983, when I was thirteen and Annabel was eleven, we became separated from Dad in different cycle rickshaws in the immense bustle of down-town Dakar, Bangladesh. Dad had put us kids in our own rickshaw, so that he and my step mum Sandi, could take photos of us from their own. But, the two flimsy vehicles had become separated in the throng and the drivers had taken different routes home across the sprawling shanti of the dusty city. The sudden stomach-churning anguish when losing a child in a shopping centre is a well-known sensation. Dad's few minutes of pacing up-and-down under the canopy of the Hilton in Dakar, before we appeared unmolested, must have been a steroidal version. Occasionally too, I've followed in his footsteps. When just still really kids in our twenties, Charlie and I paid serious money to stay at the Mount Lavinia, Dad and Sandi's favourite hotel in Colombo. This was partly because of its gently evocative colonial heritage, having been first built by the British Governor for his darling wife Lavinia, but unbeknown to Charlie, I'd had an unhealthy fascination with a food reaction Dad had there, where after eating the cuttlefish, he'd developed a tumescence of such epic proportions and duration, that he could have clubbed a herd of animals to death with it. After two nights of ordering the cuttlefish, I decided that it was a one-off.

My father wasn't some kind of unshaven, hard drinking troublemaker in the Humphrey Bogart character mould, as the stereotype might suggest. He was urbane and warm, but had just held onto the sense of mischief and irreverence that most of us enjoy in childhood. This spanned his career. After Laker had become a large airline, he received a written warning. A memo had been sent to all pilots explaining that a serious issue had come to the management's attention and that the playing of board

67

games was strictly prohibited whilst a pilot was on duty and flying an aeroplane. So, it was a drunken misjudgement, when Dad spotted the fleet captain in a hotel bar and asked for the letter J back for his scrabble set. When in management at Virgin Atlantic, he'd been delighted by the smart Alec who'd got a name shortlisted in the staff naming of an aeroplane competition. At that time, each 747 of the Virgin fleet had the moniker 'Maiden' on its fuselage, beneath a flying lady. So there was Maiden Voyager, Mystic Maiden etcetera. A brand-new aircraft was to take Richard Branson on the airline's inaugural flight to Tokyo and Dad had his fingers crossed that 'Maiden Japan' might make it onto the side of the plane. His wish came true. Like father, like son perhaps. I was asked to organise the renaming of the government body, English Nature and was similarly delighted, come the day when the board were to choose from a shortlist, that the 'Wildlife And Nature Conservation Agency' had made it to the cut, but sadly it fell at the last hurdle.

Even as the aircraft moved from clockwork, to digital, to fly-by-wire, he did not let up. Once he showed me a plastic tap complete with a small suction cup that he would very occasionally stick onto the middle one of many plasma screens built into the near sci-fi control panel of the newest 747. If the in-flight attendant running the first class compartment and the flight deck was a novice, he would make use of the litre-and-a-half bottle of mineral water stowed in the cupholder on the outside of his seat, by filling up a plastic cup with water, putting it beneath the tap and adding a drip to the tap for good measure. When the flight attendant stuck their head around the door, he would mention that the tap was dripping and ask for another cup. In an equivalent to a proxy, on-the-job, airline Mensa test, he would keep the same routine going through a transatlantic flight, until the attendant twigged.

Flying an airliner, one might think, is a serious business with serious responsibilities, but Dad's capability as a pilot was never in question. He was a real pro, of the old school. He had been taught by wartime flyers and lived a career where his chosen occupation changed almost beyond recognition. As with the dinosaurs, his type is now extinct. By his retirement, the world was teeming with regulations and with people. The flimsy panel that once separated the cockpit and the cabin was now a locked, ballistic door. The skies had become aerial motorways and the airports were towns in themselves.

He was a wonderful colleague, a great, loyal friend and a devoted husband to my step mum, but either through nature or nurture, he was never in truth, going to be a best-in-class Dad. The single piece of advice that I remember him giving me was to adopt Long Island Iced Tea as my cocktail of choice, because it is likely to have a shot more than the others. But, no one can have it all in life. He may not have been the kind of dad to stay with his kids, stand on the touchline, help you move house, put up shelves, do you a spreadsheet for car finance, or bail you out if you were skint, but there are plenty of dads like that. Not everyone could boast the following though... I've walked into bars on three different continents, in Africa, America and Asia beside my father, where I've watched the barman raise his head, crack a big smile and exclaim,

"Hey George, how the hell have you been doing?"

His stories were never written, so like most of us, his history will remain untold. I'd often implored him, but as he'd say down the phone,
"Who would want to read about that guff?"

Bob is Andy - Give or Take?

Part 1: Bob, Andy & Guy

There are just two books in print with my name on the
cover. When I say, books, they are more pamphlets, if
compared to the works of a serious author, both in weight
and content. Referring to them as novellas is a trick that
I've adopted to conceal the fact that, in literary terms, they
are just grains of sand on a wide, meandering beach.
Despite knowing this, there's more than enough vanity in
me to look up every book review ever written about them.
Mostly it's good for the ego, as it's generally our friends
who buy them, or at least, they are the ones who feel duty-
bound to write a review. So, the online reviews are
reminiscent of the enthusiastic pats on the back one would
get after delivering an adequate Best Man's or Maid of
Honour's speech.
This summer, I spotted a new review, which was too
generous to have been written by a stranger, from a guy
called Bob. My brother-in-law Robert is a Rob, not a Bob
and on checking my phone contacts list, I deemed it
unlikely that the emergency dentist that I'd once used in
Camden, in the late nineties, for an early-hours
consultation, was the contributor. Bob the-back-street-
Dentist, Camden (as my phone files him) was more of a
Marquis De Sade, or Waterboarding for Beginners kind of

guy anyway. As an aside, my current dentist is called Mr Peacock. Nothing amusing here. But he is part of a dental practice called Dentith and Dentith. How can I be the only one in the house to find this funny?

Back to Bob, or more importantly, who is Bob? I found out that getting on Bob's trail was only a click away. All you have to do is open the little profile image. In Bob's case it was just the slightly creepy standard, modern-day silhouette, but it led me straight into the lair of the reviewer and hey presto, to a little treasure trove of other reviews. Reading other people's reviews could become quite a gratifying hobby. When listed against a product, they offer you little insight, but when listed against the person, it's a totally different story. As an amateur sleuth, you get to do the kind of profiling that the people at Amazon and other analysts the world over do on you about the products you buy and the lifestyle you live. It is only a short stretch of imagination to try out what it feels like being a police psychologist. I mean, what other dark and dangerous obsessions might reside inside Bob - a man who is prepared to write six reviews about the deficiencies of AEG fridge hinges?

The ensuing detective work went as follows. Bob had recently purchased a Steampunk long coat. Every piece of tech equipment that he had apparently ever bought had a review starting with the pithy opening of "Not Fit For Purpose". There were the several particularly readable tirades about the failings of AEG fridge hinges. Amidst it all was one particularly scathing, highly entertaining and possibly larcenous review of an obscure novel. I felt that I was getting warm before hitting on the clincher. It was a glowing review of a niche rock band, referring to a gig in

72

the Roundhouse in London. When you are approaching fifty, the number of your friends who go out gigging tends to dwindle, but to his credit, our friend Andy has managed to keep up a work-rate of seeing an average of thirty bands a year. Bob was Andy. I contacted Andy, expressing surprise at his Amazon moniker and copied his wife Helen, with a suggestion that the AEG reviews might be useful, should she ever need grounds for a divorce.

As ever with Andy, and this is something that never ceases to amaze me because he is a busy and stressed business executive, his WhatsApp, text, Facebook and Twitter never miss a beat. The response was nearly instantaneous. It was about half a page of text. The email unravelled as follows:

So, there is a story behind Bob.

About twenty-five years ago I met a guy called Kirk Brown, while on holiday in Turkey. He was a fat Canadian, but had a lot of interesting stories, most of which revolved around the many celebrities he knew. He claimed to know them through family connections to film and music and it all seemed quite plausible, perhaps because the alternative was that he was lying outrageously.

Back in London, he was clearly involved in the restaurant scene and he introduced me and the people I lived with at the time, to some amazing restaurants, including meeting chefs and owners. He was also an excellent cook and taught me a few dishes which I still cook.

There was always a lot going on with him. He had stuff shipped to London which was stuck in customs. He was writing a book that was an official follow up to Zen and the Art of Motorcycle Maintenance, etc.

Anyway, he hatched a plan to visit a restaurant in Spain. It was a very famous place at the time and he had a contact with Air Canada who could get us seats on an 'empty leg' plane for a nominal fare and he'd arranged to set up a lunch at this place etc etc. Added to that, a couple of his celebrity pals were coming along - KD Lang and Brian Green (from Beverley Hills 90210). He needed some cash in advance, so I paid him £330 for the three of us that were going.

I never saw him again. After a few weeks of no contact, I called the restaurant he'd most recently been associated with and the manager complained that he hadn't seen him for weeks either and Kirk owed them money too.

Now, as you know, I bear grudges. I never stopped looking for Kirk fucking-Brown and about five years ago I found him. He was in prison. Here is the link…

"Teacher conned out of £150,000 after son-in-law poses as viscount"

A teacher has told how she was conned out of hundreds of thousands of pounds after her son-in-law posed as a viscount and spent the money on his lavish lifestyle. Nicola Young, 66, was tricked into investing £150,000 in non-existent businesses dreamed up by Kirk Brown, who changed his name by deed poll to Vizconde von Hoehen de Bessarabia.

Brown, 46, pretended to own a shipping firm and told the primary school teacher he was buying a private jet and a £30 million home in Regent's Park, London.

Mrs Young, a grandmother-of-four said Brown later calmly told her: "I'm sorry I'm a congenital liar, it's like a gambling addiction."

He used her money to finance stays in luxury hotels, regular flights to Los Angeles and publishing a book, which he claimed was to be made into a film. She has now been forced to return to work as a supply teacher to pay off her debts".

It turns out that Kirk was a con man and we got off lightly. He had in fact, written a book, so as a petty act of revenge, I decided to give it a shitty review and expose his criminality. Before doing so I changed my profile name to Bob so he couldn't trace me. I never changed it back.
I still search for the fucker now, so I can get him for real.
Cheers, Andy.

The minor mystery of why Andy has the pseudonym of Bob was now solved. On thanking Andy for his interesting correspondence, he replied simply,

"That was just the tip of the shitberg."

We agreed that Kirk needed hunting down, along with the small-time con artist who scammed me out of £750, with a phoney mobility scooter.

To paraphrase, revenge should be served cold. When the opportunity arises, it should be served in the form of chilled porcelain. Our friend Guy was diddled when buying a house. It was one of those depressing stories where the seller had cynically ripped him off, but the police told him that they weren't interested, because it was a civil issue. Then the bank refused to help claw the money back, because it was against the rules. Then his solicitor advised him to take it on the chin, because retaliation would be criminal. So, Guy moved on. Time as they say, is a great healer. Guy got married and we became friends when we met at prenatal classes a little later. I helped out when he moved to a larger family home as a second baby was on the way. It was a good property purchase, but some work needed to be done, particularly to the downstairs bathroom which retained an avocado suite. There was a decent chance that the fashion cycle might soon revolve full circle bringing avocado back on-trend, but the same was unlikely to be true for the etched-in skid marks on the toilet. The suite was replaced and when the work was done, a collection of chipped avocado ceramics was piled up in front of his garage door. The obvious next step was a Saturday morning trip to the local dump for disposal, but having kept tabs on the man who had ripped him off years before, Guy loaded up his car in the middle of the night, parked by a narrow back alley between two rows of Victorian terraced houses, checked that the coast was clear, dragged each porcelain component along the path and one-large-item-at-a-time, he dumped the whole lot over the fence of his quarry. I'm tickled by this, because it's not hard to imagine the outstretched arms, the perplexed face and the "What-The-Fucks?" of the home owner, as he came out to survey his back garden the following morning.

Part 2: Giving and Taking is not Binary

Giving and taking is not binary, it's a spectrum. I've been mulling this thought over and mentally placing along it, people I know. Mum would be an outlier as she'd give everything, including an organ to anyone in need. There are others I know and like dearly, but with whom you would

76

not want to be sharing a plane ride if there was only one parachute. A vague exception to the giving-and-taking spectrum did pop to mind, from the overfull mental waste bin that now occupies most of the space between my ears. Back in the day, when I did a short stint on the periphery of The City, I was in touch with a college friend who worked at a nearby investment bank. Surprisingly, Dom was enjoying his time working at the now defunct Warburg's, in the audit department. The audit bit of the job sounded deadly, but the department also had the word 'investigations' in its title, which is where there was an occasional flash of intrigue. One evening over an after work pint, Dom described an ongoing in-house investigation of a non-financial nature. There were sinister happenings on one of the higher floors of the bank's London HQ, where the more senior brass was stationed. Over a longish period of time, someone unknown had been visiting the executive toilets and taking a dump on a toilet seat. However, the kicker was that he or she (and let's face it, it was going to be a he) would add a flourish, by rolling a new £50 note into a cone and sticking it, pointy-end first, into his own 'doings'. This sticks in my mind partly because it is so psychologically screwy, but also because it purposely plays with the notion of give-and-take. It's the turd version of a Banksy graffiti piece - that makes you think.

I was trained in business never to give anything without receiving something in return. This of course, is the first rule of negotiation. If life offered up an unwarranted windfall, it followed that it should be snapped up no matter what, because this was just taking a bit of 'the smooth' in a world where there would be at least an equal amount of 'the rough'. Thus, I learned to trade, but it infected everything.

A favour granted was a favour owed. The loaning of a chainsaw would enable the borrowing of a leaf blower. Paying for dinner would leave a small mental debt and so on.

By the time that you reach your mid-forties, you are meant to be on the top of your game, a provider, the person doing the giving. Giving is a proxy signpost of success. If you have the capacity to do what is necessary in life *and* help others, then atta' boy, you must be doing something right. But a form of moral trading took a quiet hold of this as well. So, I'd complainingly brag about the amount of tax my business paid. I'd raise funds for a cause most years and sit on the board of a charity, all in the barely conscious knowledge that it was tax deductible, would help keep me fit, might improve my CV and could make one's social media look good. Any one still thinking of sharing that plane ride where there's only one parachute aboard might want to reconsider.

Then one day I got the nasty diagnosis and this worldview began to pivot. The first shove that set things in motion involved walking into a gift shop in my nearby town. An elderly German lady was talking earnestly with the shop owner, so I waited a little uncomfortably and perused the Nepali gifts that were on haphazard display around the bijou emporium called Shangri La. I had been looking for some help with meditation which had involved Googling around the local vicinity looking for a teacher. Finding nothing, I had explored websites that offered courses or long retreats. Fearing over-commitment and seeing a touch of the Moonies about every one of them, the research had drawn a blank, before a friend mentioned that one could do worse than popping into Shangri La and striking up a conversation with its owner. So, as the German lady bid farewell, I swapped a couple of pleasantries with the man behind the counter, before diving in and asking if he knew anything about meditation? He was about my age, short, but muscular with a face of the Buddha and was called Udaya. We talked for a few minutes and although I had planned not to, because revealing one's cards and showing weakness is considered a bad strategy, I ended up explaining my predicament in full. I sensed that the conversation was nearing its conclusion, so was already running a second train of thought about the next steps, when Udaya said,

"Okay, I'll come".

A look of confusion was enough for him to elaborate.

"I'll come to your house this evening and help you to meditate."

Sensing a trap, I began to row back. I mean, what was the deal here? What was I signing up to? How much would this cost? How could I let someone that I'd only met for fifteen minutes into my home? Seeing question marks multiplying in the ether between us, Udaya allowed me a moment to string a few polite phrases together that could have boiled down into a less polite, "so what's the deal?" But there was no deal as Udaya set out the position as he saw it, I wanted to meditate. He had been meditating for twenty years. I needed help, which he could give. The matter was urgent, so he would close up at 5.30pm, get on his bicycle and be at my home by 5.45pm.

I instinctively countered by asking about money and when satisfied that no payment was being requested, I moved on to the softer areas, seeking to establish ways in which one might compensate for help in the calming the mind department, so as to even-up the trade and not end up indebted. Floundering around in uncharted territory, it became clear that the loaning out of a chainsaw was not an appropriate exchange for a meditation lesson and that there was nothing that needed to be done other than to suck up my own pride, re-organise a belief system built over twenty five years, and accept the offer for what it was - an act of giving and of kindness. Though I felt like a wrestler banging the canvas in submission at the time, it needn't have been so hard. Since then acts of kindness have multiplied and although it still takes effort, I've been trying to accept them for what they are.

People nearly always do nice stuff for you because they want to, not because they feel they should and not because they want to snare you or get something in return. In the early days of being unwell, I hid behind a quote from somewhere that said, "there is nothing as spirit crushing as other people's pity". It matched where I was at the time, but this was either accidental or wilful confusion on my behalf between pity and kindness. These two words might be siblings in that they are both the offspring of compassion, but pity is a complex word laced with sorrow. Pity also often requires an object, that is - something to be pitied. Kindness, by contrast is straightforward. The word brims with warmth and generosity. Learning to accept kindness, in my experience, is not easy, but it is oddly liberating. Needless to say, the reverse is also true, in that any giving that I now do is less loaded and more enjoyable too.

It's still easy to be tested on this stuff though. Being offered help from people who are not fortunate is hard as is taking donations from minors! This last year presented a grand example, but we have to go back to 2014 to get the full force of the context. It was the June of that summer that our world unravelled. I had no obvious ailments, save for a slightly weak left thumb and leg muscles that twitched day and night. Several months of tests had yielded no positive results, so after a battery of new medical examinations I was not prepared for the diagnosis of Motor Neurone Disease, which was delivered brutally and hit like a hammer blow. If we were not dizzied enough by the news, I was called into hospital just forty-eight hours later and told to be there immediately. There was no emergency, just that a bed in the neuro ward had become free and on seeing the space on her rounds, the consultant thought it opportune to slot me in for some exploratory therapy. Unaware of this, I wondered if it might be better to bypass the hospital and drive straight to the undertakers. Before staying there, the words Addenbrooke's Hospital, Cambridge had conjured up state-of-the-art visions in my mind. These were dispelled by ward R2 which appeared to be the working TV set of a sixties' hospital sitcom. It was almost reassuring. I'd not stayed in a hospital since I was ten, so save for a pile of digital equipment, everything else was almost unchanged. It was all made less appealing by a spell of warm weather outside that must have coincided with the man in the maintenance room accidentally pushing the boiler to full power, then accidentally pulling the handle off it.

A neurology ward is not a place for the faint of heart (that's the cardiac ward). Granted, it might be less whiffy than the gastro ward and less phlegmy than at ENT, but it could be the neuro ward that wins the prize for bewildering diversity. At around 8.00pm I was given the middle bed in a ward of six where half of the beds faced the other. To the left was a young man in a coma which had followed a seizure. He lay motionless as various machines beeped, wined and gurgled.

To the right was a dodgy, weasley looking geezer who had been hit by a dustcart. Ahead and to the left was an older and obviously kindly man in the late stages of dementia. He waved gently each time our eyes met, which was okay for the first fifteen seconds. Directly across the way was a man being readied for a major operation and to the far right was a strong looking fella in his fifties, who was a DJ by trade, but who had attained some celebrity by being the first person to have a small device wired inside his brain to dampen the effects of Parkinson's Disease. He was in to have his batteries changed. As the obvious ward boss, he asked what I was in for. On hearing he said that I would be given preferential treatment, because in neuro terms, I had the 'big boys' disease'. Not reassured by this, I spent an unhappy first few hours listening to the rhythms playing out on the machines wired into the poor man next to me. At about 11.00pm, I was woken from a doze by a consultant swinging the blue curtains closed around my bed whilst introducing himself. His voice lowered slightly to ensure that the curtain provided absolute privacy, he took a seat on the chair and re-explained the awful prognosis that I had been given less than two days before. He went through the proposed therapy, explained that the odds of its success were firmly against me, then shook my hand and bid me goodnight. It wasn't.

A tortuous week ensued. The drugs were fed in intravenously through the day but were gloopy so had to be compensated with a saline drip in the other arm, leaving dangling tubes to the left and right. Predicted headaches came and went, but these could have just been the results of the relentless heating system. Alarmingly, one might wake up to find a gap in the ward where there had been a bed with a person in it. It was no use asking after the patient as the nurses weren't allowed to say.

On day three, a nurse casually put a small bottle into my hand, explained that she would be unplugging me, suggested that I make use of the time by having a shower, but then revealed herself by telling me to wash vigorously all over twice, in fact to keep washing until the contents of the bottle ran out. I offered enquiring eyes and was told in a whisper that the daily swabs had found MRSA in the ward and that unfortunately, I had been sharing medical machines with the host. I looked at the little scrote to my right and glared. Seeing that I was getting unplugged, he offered me a weak smile, then asked if I might be allowed to go downstairs and get him in a packet of cigarettes.

By day four it was all getting too much. A catheter change was due, so I begged the sister for a little R&R time, just to be allowed to go to the concourse and perhaps stand in the doorway to sample fresh air. She agreed that I could abscond for an hour or so. So, dressed in hospital pyjamas, with arms bandaged like a recovering addict, I made it to the lift and pressed the round button with G on it. As the doors opened, the scenes were similar to the ones you see at a regional airport on a bank holiday weekend. The lift wells were crowded with heads as people squeezed to get themselves up to the higher floors of the hospital. Looking for a bit of space I pushed through the crowd and walked straight into a familiar looking petite, blonde woman of my age.

"What are you doing here?" asked Tracey, staring up at the hollowed out, unshaven version of an old friend.

"What are you doing here?" I responded, looking back at the exhausted and harrowed features of an old friend.

I'm not sure who went first as we stood frozen in the melee of the lift well. It's quite possible that I gabbled, explaining the recent diagnosis, seeking comfort. If this was the case, I wish I hadn't because Tracey started by saying,

"Have you not heard about Seb?"

"No", I said, "What's happened?"

Tracey looked at me surprised. I should have known. We had all been good friends until life and child-rearing had taken us in different directions, when we had two infant girls and she and Nick had had twin boys. Even so, we lived nearby to the same small town, with its small-town gossip, where everyone knows everyone. Some three months before I had heard a grizzly headline on the BBC of a nine-year-old boy falling under a bus in Norfolk, but hate the sensationalism as the media twists someone's personal, family tragedy with alliteration and plot-lines for its own benefit, so I'd switched off.

Tracey's eyes welled.

"Seb went under a bus on the A47 in April. Had you not heard about it? It's been all over the news."

The world shrank.

Part 3: Seb

Seb had been at a rugby tournament in Norfolk. He and his brother Ben had both been important players in the local junior team which had enjoyed an impressive run of success through the winter. Their dad, Nick, is a rugby devotee, so had accompanied his sons on the day out. The preparations for the return coach trip home had involved the usual kerfuffle of colleting kit, herding kids and checking numbers before the tired diesel engine of the coach rasped into life. The coach had beeped as the driver made multiple attempts for the door hydraulics to lock into place, as had happened earlier in the day. Though the sun was just beginning to dip to the west, there was still plenty of daylight ahead and the mood was good as they set out towards the big skies of the Fens. Once well underway, Seb left his seat and walked down the steps to the onboard toilet at the centre of the bus. It was occupied, so as he waited, he leant against the emergency exit door. The coach was travelling at speed. The faulty door had not caught on its lock. In the next instant, the path of Seb's young life so very nearly stopped dead as he was pulled out of the coach and under its wheels.

There is a book to be written by someone else about the extraordinary teamwork, the incredible medical technologies, the community support and the inspiring, heroic parenting that swung into motion in the seconds, minutes, hours and months that followed. Only Seb's staggering resilience and instinct to survive eclipses this. Seb 'died' that day and three further times in the weeks that followed. In the first four months, he endured twenty-nine operations, each averaging close to four hours in duration. A number were unplanned, life-saving 'crash operations'. There is a paradox for me that is too stark not to trail. The 'bad luck' of this awful event is absolute - without question. It is a one in a million tragedy. The chances of surviving such an accident were incredibly small too. Whichever random or chaotic forces made it happen are equalled by the chain of events that helped Seb to live. He would have died in the first minutes following the accident if an unlikely set of circumstances had not unfolded immediately.

An experienced nurse, who was holidaying in Norfolk and travelling in the opposite direction, spotted Seb lying on the verge and pulled over. Nearly overwhelmed by what she found as Seb made an instinctive effort to stand, but then collapsed, she was joined on the carriageway within a matter of seconds by the trauma consultant from King's Lynn hospital, who was in the queue behind the coach. Between them they located Seb's femoral artery, with the doctor pinching it tightly in an attempt to staunch the blood loss. A paramedic was the next on the scene. The contents of his estate car provided the materials that the doctor and nurse needed to keep Seb alive through the long minutes as they waited for the ambulance. Without the combination of equipment and expertise, each person would have been impotent. As it was, every bag of plasma in the paramedic's car had been used by the time the ambulance arrived. Seb was rushed to King's Lynn where the area's best vascular surgeon happened to be on duty for the critical operation to tie-off of the artery. Without let-up, Seb was put into an ambulance and driven to Cambridge. En route, he went into cardiac arrest, but was resuscitated. Meanwhile that day, a rostering fluke had put the best-of-the-best together on call at Addenbrooke's for overnight emergency surgery. One of the renowned surgeons later confided in Nick, that he had never seen his even more esteemed colleague so near to losing her cool as she was that night - as the team of vascular, orthopaedic, neuro and plastic surgeons battled on to bring Seb back from the brink.

Nick, who had lived through every traumatising moment of the accident's aftermath was joined by Tracey at Addenbrooke's. By the time Tracey and I had walked into each other in the lift well on that hot day in June, they had already spent two months camped there. Although by no means out of the woods, Seb was now stable enough to be housed in the children's surgical ward and had become a hospital favourite. On my own stays and appointments there, I would visit Seb and marvel at what we can achieve as a race when we are at our finest. A positive calm hummed in the air alongside the equipment. At the centre was a nine-year-old boy showing astonishing resilience as the extent of the injuries and the resulting infections revealed themselves and as the operations continued.

After four months, all that could be done by surgeons had been done. Seb was moved first to a post-operative rehabilitation centre in Cambridgeshire and then to a more specialist version of the same in Surrey for intensive rehab. The coach's wheels had crushed and effectively severed his right leg. The fall to the tarmac at fifty miles an hour had left two significant head injuries, leading to some brain and nerve damage with an unknown long-term impact. These and other serious wounds were the base-camp from where the next stage of the struggle would begin. With Nick and Tracey in the lead they moved onwards. Aspects of Seb's physical recovery continued to confound the medics. Incisions from operations healed at improbable speeds. With every system in his body on overdrive including his stem cells, nodules of bone began to grow from his femur as his body made attempts to re-grow a leg, requiring further procedures to remove them.

Then came the happy milestone of the full-time move back to home so that the family could be properly reunited, but this marked the beginning of the next hill-climb which would establish Seb back into the everyday world and get him in school again. Slowly he re-built strength, speech and coordination. Meanwhile, money was raised for state-of-the-art equipment and his home was modified. In the three years that followed, Seb moved from a wheelchair to crutches and on to a prosthetic leg. The day that I first saw Seb up on his new titanium leg, I asked him how he was getting on with it and if he had had any falls.

"What do you think?" was the response, accompanied by a big grin.

As Seb also caught up on his schoolwork and began playing wheelchair sports, I was moving in the other direction, starting with the loss of hand use, then a pronounced limp with dropped ankles, before succumbing and moving into a wheelchair.

One day Seb and I discussed the subject of wheelchairs. Despite discomfort and fatigue, Seb explained that he was doing everything he could to spend as little time in one as possible. We commiserated with each other about how miserable and isolating it can be, sitting facing forward and at crotch level. I showed Seb a picture of a state-of-the-art power wheelchair that, like a transformer, can lift its seated passenger to a standing position, then thought nothing more of it. This in-passing conversation must have struck a chord, because soon after Nick called to ask if I would mind if Seb did some fundraising for me to help towards buying a stand-up wheelchair.

Part 4: Life is Full of Lump-in-the-Throat Moments

Life is full of lump-in-the-throat moments. As we get older, many of us can barely get through the ad breaks on telly without having to gulp, but even so one would have to be a particularly hardened individual not to feel an upwelling of emotion when a fourteen-year-old amputee asks to raise money for your own wheelchair. Amongst the emotional concoction, there is helplessness, embarrassment and even a slim, uncomfortable vein of indignation, but these intermingle with a sense of kinship and empathy, plus the buoyancy one gets with support from another person, even if that person is really just a kid. There is a temptation to withdraw, by bringing down the emotional shutters, but with a modicum of courage even a repressed middle-aged Englishman like me can hang on inside the emotional melee for a few more moments. Like the swirling of a decent pint of Guinness, the chaos soon subsides and the froth turns into something more substantial and nourishing. I began to feel grateful, not the kind of grateful you get when the DPD delivery man *doesn't* throw your parcel over the gate, I mean properly grateful. Gratitude was considered by Cicero as the well-spring of all positive emotions. Today psychologists and even neuroscientists see gratitude as the cornerstone of good mental-health. It's taken me most of a lifetime to begin properly to channel it, but even if it sometimes splutters, I'm better off for sampling an occasional deeply-felt sense of gratitude. So, after a little cry in the toilet and a word with myself in the mirror, I accepted Seb's help, gratefully.

The plan was uncomplicated, Seb would train up and get sponsored to handcycle the twenty-three-mile undulating dirt track around Rutland Water. It is sometimes said, mainly by Australians, that we Brits are good at sitting down sports. By definition, handcycling is a sitting down sport, but it is not for the faint hearted. Outside wheelchairs and handcycles, I can't think of any other cardio-vascular means of propulsion that is not substantially powered through the legs. If you ever watch competitive sailing on the TV there are always glimpses of muscular sailors

furiously using both arms to turn the two-handled winch
that lifts the sails, but this short burst only lasts a few
seconds. Handcycling is hard work on a smooth, flat
surface. On a hilly and uneven terrain, it is a gnarly,
physical challenge and this is before considering that one's
bum is in a sling seat that's only three inches above any
jagged rocks.

Seb and his brother Ben swung into action raising money
and training for the event. With their Dad as coach and
spurred on by a group of teenage friends they raised more
and more money, before settling down to the actual task on
a breezy summer's day in June and achieving their
objective. It was all done in a carnival atmosphere, ignoring
the physical challenge. His family and a band of friends
cycled with Seb along the way and he completed his circuit
on a section of smooth tarmac with his biceps and shoulders
abulge. After a short celebratory ice cream, he was asleep a
few minutes after getting into the car to go home. The
whole thing had been a triumph. Though I felt faintly
embarrassed on the day, it was the sense of support and the
feeling of gratitude that lingered on.

Part 5: Sainey

In the Autumn of this same year, my little family took a
holiday to the Gambia in West Africa. We rented a
bungalow in a resort in the off-season and as a result found
the place almost empty, except for many dozens of staff
working on half pay through the rainy season and a few
neighbours that worked for NGOs or were holidaying from
other parts of Africa. One day part way through our
vacation two Dutch couples arrived. They caused a stir in

the resort. Security guards, gardeners and bar staff all pitched in to drag trolley loads of stacked cardboard boxes to their chalet. After making an enquiry, we found out that this same group had been taking their annual vacation in the Gambia for many years. They were different from your average holidaymaker though. The most obvious thing was that the main room at their chalet was filled, floor to ceiling with boxes and only a narrow cardboard passageway gave access to their bedrooms. Some of their ten-day holiday would be spent lounging by the pool, but the balance would be used to distribute a container load of supplies that they shipped out in advance every year to coincide with their stay. As no-nonsense Dutch people, they would use some of their holiday to provide essential supplies directly to a school and two clinics that they had somehow adopted. These guys weren't rich, they weren't flash, but they had long ago realised that, if they raised around two thousand Euros each year, they could change the life chances and health of many hundreds of people for the better. Their English was very patchy, but in discussion it became clear that most of their fundraising back home was done alongside working nine-to-five jobs and it involved collecting small sums. In Britain, we are very generous not only in the frequency with which we give to charities, but the amount that we are prepared to part with. So, when I gave some English notes for their home-spun charity, they were surprised by the pile of Gambian currency that was returned to them across the glass of the local bureau de change.

Seeing an opportunity, I resolved to go home and raise a bit of cash for them, knowing just how far it would go. It had been impressive to see how the Hulp4Gambia team navigated the endemic corruption in the country. Whereas a big charity might suffer losses through the chain, our friends held onto every centime and were providing it to those who needed help right at the source. If they were stopped by police with the minibus full of aid, they would not pay a bribe to pass the checkpoint, but instead would hand out three or four cheap cigarette lighters to get free passage. On returning to a wintery England it was approaching the season of goodwill, so we did not have to break sweat to raise some money through our family and friends. Our modest total bought all new desks and some new books for the school, but then also provided a staggeringly long list of basic medical supplies to one of the clinics, including many thousands of antimalarial doses.

I kept in touch with Peter from Hulp4Gambia as he was keen to send photographs of everything that had been achieved through the fundraiser. Using Google translate, we picked through and made sense of each other's emails. One photograph showed the family of the person on whom they had come to rely as their fixer in the Gambia. It was taken in a small breeze block backyard with orange African dust under foot. It must have been late in the day, as shadows cast themselves across a tiny yard. I can imagine the black kites circling in the vicinity as the vultures soared on the thermals high in the sky. The parents looked proud with their arms on the shoulders of their two children. The youngest had a beaming moon face. Beneath his grin was a clean green T-shirt that over-sailed a pair of baggy tracksuit bottoms. Neither the T-shirt, nor trousers could disguise just how bowed Sainey's little legs were. Both legs bent outwards in arks from the hips right down to the ankles. Peter had already made contact with a Dutch medical charity that sends teams to Africa to perform surgery on the needy. The previous summer, the orthopaedic surgeons had seen Sainey's bow legs during a clinic in the Gambian Capital, Banjul. They had confirmed that his condition was operable and that subject to some further evaluation a few months ahead, they would include him in their schedule of operations in the following year. Peter wrote that he and his colleagues were planning to raise the money for the operation in the intervening period. I asked how much. The answer was three hundred Euros for the operation and perhaps fifty more to provide money for Sainey's family to travel to the clinic and stay with him for a couple of weeks. Though slow on some decisions, there was no reason to beat around the bush on this one. I replied that we would take care of the costs of the operation. Next, I opened the blank email pane and sent the photograph, accompanied with the story of Sainey's bow legs to half a dozen friends, explaining that I had made a personal commitment to pay for the correcting of one of his legs, but that if no one else intervened, the poor little kid would be walking in circles for the rest of his life. I have no idea why the big aid charities don't use the same ruse in their own fundraising, because we hit the target in less than forty-five minutes, (even if the term 'sicko' was used by someone in the donor group). The operation happened just a couple of weeks ago. As I type, Sainey is sitting in a hospital bed in Banjul with two straight legs plastered to the thighs and braced apart with a big splint. The operation was a success and he looks bright and well.

In the moment, whilst I studied the pictures of Sainey on the hospital bed, with the lively patterned curtains blowing in the wind behind, there seemed some God sent irony snaking through these events that I still can't quite put my finger on now. There is a probably a parable in here

93

somewhere about the teenage boy with one leg, who inspired a man with failing legs to fix a boy's bow legs. If there is, the take home message would be about compassion and gratitude. We may live in a world of give and take, but as I'm figuring out, it is a better place for everyone if we give in to ourselves and feel grateful.

Being Disabled Sucks

Occasionally people ask me 'how come I've ended up in a wheelchair'. There's a split second where I want to say that something dramatic or heroic put me in the chair, but after a brief pause, I give in and tell the truth.
"There's a disease eating up my nervous system which in turn causes the muscles to waste away."
Then, everyone looks a bit awkward for a second. One day, given a suitable situation, it would be fun to try something different when the same question is posed. I'd take a brooding deep breath and then pause to summon up a gravelly, monotone voice and fix my gaze into the middle distance.
"I was hit in the back by a sniper, back in 2013..."
"Forty minutes in and out of consciousness, lying in the dirt of a poppy field in the Korangal Valley,"
"Taliban all around..."
"Twice resuscitated in the helicopter back to Bagram."
"Twice more on the medivac to the hospital in Italy."
"No way of fixing it. The scan showed a broken spine..."
"And a grenade up my ass."
I'd then pause for effect, lift my dead-eye gaze to those of the inquirer and nod slowly. The confused person at the checkout or in the parking booth would nod back in bemusement whilst fumbling for the right change, or the

blushing optician would flip the lens in and out of the
comedy glasses and continue,
"Better now?... or better now?"
It would be just as awkward, but at least it would be fun for
me and offer a proper conversational dividend to the asker.

Being disabled sucks. It really does. I reckon that even
those people who have developed great empathy probably
struggle to comprehend the panoply of suffering, big and
small, that people with disabilities endure. As someone
with below average empathy, my journey into disability has
been a brutal lesson in life. Having been dealt a hand of
difficult cards with the words 'progressive muscle wasting
disease' written across them, I have watched my progress
from minor through to severe disability. In the early stages
it was easy to hide. I looked and acted fine to all but the
cognoscenti. Most bits of me worked as you might expect
them to and the bits that didn't could be masked by using
substitute techniques or tricks. Buttons could be swapped
for poppers, pretty loops of ribbon hung from drawer knobs
at home and grip tape could be attached to slippery handles.
Even then, I'd occasionally be found out. Sometimes an
entire torso would appear from the car window to permit
my teeth to grasp the protruding ticket offered teasingly by
the machine at the entrance to a car park. Or Charlie might
grab the pen and sign my name on a form when the bank
manager's back was turned.
Then came the period where we found that I could not walk
in shallow water because my feet flippered as the legs
pulled upwards and my wrists drooped obviously in family
photographs. These and other mechanical failures were
masked for a time by orthotic splints; a composite of
plastic, neoprene, bandages, hinges, straps, gel pads and

Velcro. In clothes and with the body-armour underneath, I continued to look and act relatively normally - knowing that without it I'd collapse like an amoeba.

But as the bigger muscles succumbed, I started to limp and stoop, becoming the disabled person that we had hidden. The equipment piled up with each visit from the occupational therapists. Drawers and cupboards were filled with ingenious aids. Most soon became obsolete within months. The bigger, heavier equipment came next and with it our home began to change too. A raised sofa and bed ushered in a replacement toilet with automatic sci-fi wash, dry, turbo-wash, oscillate and massage functions, controlled by a remote that was more complex than the television's. After that it was the ubiquitous disabled bathroom refit, looking like a hybrid hospital room and gym. Over the period, we had collected a wheelchair and two sizes of mobility scooter too, so my former office also brimmed. Finally, the really big and really expensive stuff came into sight in the form of a twenty-six stone power wheelchair, a specialist riser recliner chair, a hoist and more. Where once I could pretend to be normal, I could no longer wash, dress, toilet, scratch an itch, or get a glass of water on my own.

When it comes to other people, there is no surprise that some are tuned in, empathetic and careful. Others are uncomfortable and a little clumsy. A few say outright stupid things. I can't think of any purposeful attempts to upset or insult, but like racism it is sometimes the quantum of micro-upsets or micro-thoughtlessnesses that build up and begin to hurt. I was speaking with a black friend of a friend called Alan recently at dinner, who said something similar. In his adult life he had only occasionally suffered direct abuse but, had long suffered thinly masked discrimination and a multitude of ongoing instances of micro-racism. In his view, the direct abuse is easier to deal with, because of its idiocy. As a boy from Croydon, being told to go home makes little sense, unless you have ventured north of the Thames. Anyhow, in a different and less tolerant dimension, the racial abuser would simply be removed from the roll-call of humanity and melted down into something more useful like engine grease or processed into fish pellets.

Thinly veiled discrimination can be called out these days too. Alan was taken away for questioning by police in the Sierra Nevada mountains, because he was carrying a snowboard and wearing ski equipment in a place where black people don't often ski. He demanded to see the captain of the police station and gave him a bollocking. It would have been a good time to use the eighties' comedy sketch punch-line and ask if he had been "charged with being in possession of curly black hair and thick lips". Similarly, the pro at his tennis club in Brighton accosted him on court, refused to accept that he was a newly paid-up member and only addressed him via his white tennis partner. Rather than punching him, Alan declined to converse through a third party, stood his ground firmly, expressed his outrage at the racism and won the moral victory, with the result that the tennis pro has toadied-up to him ever since.

Given the above, my own issues with other people pale. Charlie has been asked on more than one occasion, whilst pushing my wheelchair if "he can walk?" She's quick enough to respond,
"He can talk, so why not ask him?"

Even then, this retort was once lost on an airport security man, who was probably deploying the larger portion of his own limited brainpower to stand on two legs himself.

A surprisingly regular occurrence on the undulating terrain near our home, when going up an incline on my power wheelchair, is to be greeted by a kindly looking, red-faced cyclist with daft comments like,

"You've got the right idea mate," or "that's cheating" or "can I have a tow?"

I normally respond with a fake smile, because it is not meant to harm, but the trouble is that it does. For me, the fantasy scenario would be, of course, to jump out of the electric wheelchair, tip them off their bicycle and power away up the hill leaving the words,

"OK fatso - you take the cripple-mobile and I'll meet you at the top," ringing in their ears.

The thing that leaves Charlie regularly speechless is being asked about my condition and getting the response,

"Oh yes - my uncle died of that".

It's a known social trick to seek common ground on any given topic, but holy-moly, this technique should really be restricted to nothing more serious than,

"Yes, I've had poisoning from Chinese food too" moments.

All this might suggest a certain martyrdom or victimhood on my part, but the truth is that I'm no less gauche than many a well-meaning dick-head. I regularly wince at a moment from the past that became part of my own repertoire of anecdotes. So good was it that I remember a crowning moment when a group of boozed-up colleagues had to hold each other up whilst the tale was energetically recounted at a late night barbeque.

Way back, when I worked for a big travel company, an unexpected promotion had come my way, but in a piece of corporate sleight of hand someone had used the chaos of a company reorganisation to slip me, the greenest general manager, a member of staff who was known to be a handful. Simon had worked for the firm, man and boy and had risen to a senior position, before an absolutely horrendous car accident on the job which had left him with deep mental scars and significant physical disability. In an act of reciprocated loyalty, the company had vowed not to betray him and through this act of generosity, it had effectively given him a job for life. All of this can be considered as just, which on most levels, it was. It wasn't however for anyone managing Simon; it was a shit-show. So, as I was the least experienced and possibly least equipped manager, Simon was perversely passed into our team and given the amorphous title of development manager.

From the get-go, I missed just how heroic it was for a disabled man, who was nearing retirement age and who already boasted more than forty years of company service, to get to work in the first place. Though living alone, Simon managed to make it in at 8.30 each morning under his own steam, by using only one side of his body. Right now, even the thought is exhausting. With an upturned collar, wonky glasses and a patchy shave, he would limp past my desk each day and offer a greeting, before swinging the large satchel slung over his back onto his own work station. Then bracing himself against something solid, he would pose his stick, use his good arm to wrestle off his suit jacket and drop into the chair. At 4.30pm, he would do the same in reverse, using his teeth to hold the collar of his jacket as he fed his bad arm in with the other, before running the gauntlet of a vast open-plan office to the entrance lobby. We worked in varying proximity for years, but to my shame, I know almost nothing of how he managed in the hours in between. It is not certain if the fault is all mine for not seeking out the man behind the disability, or his for being a terrific pain in the arse, with or without disability. From the vantage point gained from twenty-three years more of life experience, I would have known that the situation was wrong on too many counts to let it lie. He needed help, lots of it, as did I. Beneath his only partially functioning exterior, he was an emotional wreck, haunted in the deep by the shadows of trauma, but boiling with frustration just beneath the surface.

I would sometimes bring up the subject of retirement, but only obliquely, because it was a known trigger point. Simon had the fourth longest service amongst the 36,000 employees of the company, but he would joke that there was plenty of time left to run in his career to make it to number one, because the company was still employing a camel guide in Egypt who had joined at thirteen years of age in 1928 and was still going strong sixty nine years later at the age of eighty two. This light-hearted quip was as far as could be got with the 'R' word and if one tried to push harder, there would be a sudden meeting with a union rep. and the HR department on the near horizon.

So, we rubbed along uncomfortably for a good long while. Low-level complaints might come in about our development manager, but I'd generally make excuses and ignore them, until they came in as a cluster or something occurred that could not easily be disregarded. Occasionally we would have to sit down to iron out some misunderstanding or another with Simon and his union rep on one side of the table and with me and an HR person on

101

the other. Simon's combination of being 'old school' and frustrated was a tricky one, particularly for younger, female staff. Then, occasionally news would filter back from a supplier or customer who had found themselves stuck on a long and uncomfortable phone call where Simon had over-shared his recollection of the car accident and its aftermath. Our sit-down meetings with HR and the carefully phrased warnings would reset things for a while at least.

We did much of the non-travel stuff in the UK arm of our big travel company. Because it was not the sales or the commercial departments, we neither sold holidays to the public, nor bought them in bulk from tour operators, cruise companies, theme parks, airlines or hotel groups. Those people who did, got great perks alongside their day jobs. Sales teams went on 'educationals' so that they could sample what they were selling, and commercial managers naturally had to go away to see what they were buying. These trips were mostly the excuse for an immense piss-up somewhere nice. If you asked after a colleague who had not been around for a few days, one might get a wink and a response that,
"Adrian has not made it back to work this week after overdoing it on the Val De Lobo educational".
Our people would roll their eyes and complain about the injustice of it all. I'd remind them that come Christmas we would get a modest payback when our suppliers began to send in a treasure trove of hampers, chocolate boxes and booze.
Even so our annual perk was dwarfed by many of our colleagues who might stagger into the office pulling a wheelie bag straight from an educational on a P&O Cruise ship, or after a whirlwind tour of the Florida theme parks.

Unable to compete directly, I fancied that we might be able to even things up a fraction by making the most of our collective charm. A couple of commercial managers in the buying-of-holidays department happened to be friends, so one year we made enquiries about how we in the boiler room might get to sample the rarefied air of the upper decks. Trips to the USA or even Spain were out of the question, but a domestic holiday company might be happy to entertain us as a friendly gesture towards our brand. The lowest hanging fruit, it turned out, was also a convenient one. The boat hire companies from the Norfolk Broads were only two or so hours' drive away and would happily have us all aboard one of their newest, luxury boats. The opportunity was seized and a diary date set. A supplier who had forgotten Christmas offered to send us a couple of boxes of refreshments to help the day go well. If the Norfolk Broads was a success, Eurostar might be our next stepping stone into the glamorous world of the educational.

We set off in the chill of daybreak early on a Thursday morning after stowing our canteen-made picnic and soft drinks beneath the minibus seats. At the arrival in Wroxham we were greeted at the boat company offices and led straight to our vessel without having to endure any sales blurb at all. This confirmed our suspicions that there was very little education in an educational. We were handed the keys to our boat and someone gave one of the more capable amongst us a demonstration of how to drive the thing. By the time I jumped aboard everyone had started to get comfortable, with the smokers already occupying the rear deck. The cruiser was very shiny, very big and almost brand-new. In fact it was the biggest, newest and most expensive addition to any of the boat hire companies on the

Norfolk Broads. We 'oohed' and 'aahed' at the comfortable cabins, the en suite bathrooms and the large communal area in the cockpit. Someone pressed a big button and the canopy slid back on its runners opening us to the grey sky with hints of promising blue above. The water foamed as the bow thrusters pushed us from our mooring and we were off, far from the monotony of office life and the clutches of the corporate world.

Though it was still a little way from midday on the boat, the team was keen to get drinking. So, the first cardboard box to be opened was one of the two boxes of refreshments that had been gifted to us. There was a moment of horror as various plastic bottles were tugged from the sleeves - all of them soft drinks. This was replaced by cheer as the second box was pulled open to reveal an entire crate of premium spirits in litre bottles. We sat chatting with our super-sized, warm gin and tonics as the boat pushed forward, passing the occasional family of swans and as the odd grebe appeared from beneath the water then disappeared again into the unknown. The boat slipped through the meanders then along the picture postcard riverside frontage of Horning, staring into the neat properties of all types with their terraces, balconies, manicured gardens, jetties and boathouses. As the boat rocked softly, we waved energetically and raised our glasses to people passing on the other side in their smaller boats, just to emphasise that for this one day we had risen to the top.

By mid afternoon, and with our meagre packed lunches largely fed to the local wildlife, much of the energy had gone out of the party and people sat in small groups red-faced and chatting at different parts of the boat. Then someone tapped me on the shoulder and said,
"I think you need to have a word with Simon".

104

I asked what was occurring and where he was.

"He's still at the back with the smokers, drinking brandy from the bottle."

At the smoking den on the low rear deck, I found Simon as described. Dressed in an open necked office shirt and black trousers, it was the width of his smile that was initially disconcerting. He beamed nonchalantly and raised a half empty bottle of Remy Martin. His wonky glasses were very seriously askew as he turned and dropped his head to look over them when I plopped down next to him on the bench. We swapped some slurred pleasantries about the day's state of affairs and the weather, before I gently prised the neck of the bottle from his hand and said something corporate sounding and probably fatuous about his seniority, that he was still representing the company and what the impressionable young'uns might be thinking. Simon slurred a genuine sounding apology, but I left before he got the chance to tell me that I was a diamond or his best mate and on departing asked a worldly lady by the name of Pam to keep a close eye on him for the remainder of the boat trip. Two of the more senior guys, Mark and Pete, had been watching from the galley, possibly in the hope of catching some kind of diplomatic incident first hand. We leaned against the kitchen units and chatted quietly about the day and about our return. The low windows showed shuttered riverbanks outside, marking that we were returning through Horning. We had made good progress on our return leg, but as the riverbank got alarmingly close for a second, I stopped mid-sentence to ask,

"Who's driving the boat?"

Pete and Mark looked at each other, then towards the cockpit and then back offering blank expressions. It turned out that Carlie, our diminutive twenty-one-old secretary from Baltimore, Maryland had taken the initiative and was now kneeling forward on the captain's chair with one hand on the wheel. Though moving past signs to the contrary, we were travelling at ramming speed whilst Carlie turned the wheel one way, then compensated by turning it back swiftly the other as the cruiser snaked. Anaesthetised by vodka and seemingly oblivious to the gestures from passing river traffic, Carlie was kneeling up with her head above the windshield offering big one-handed waves to passers-by accompanied by loud Jewish-American "Hi y'all's". Forty-five minutes later our boat was back in Wroxham with Pete or Mark at the helm. We cruised in like pro's, slamming the engine into reverse so that the ship stopped dead. Then a mixture of the current and the bow thrusters placed us so gently into position, that the rubber fenders didn't even squeak as we parallel parked. Anyone observing us disembarking this cruiser might however have easily mistaken our dishevelled group for seagoing passengers who had endured three days and nights in a mighty storm crossing the Bay of Biscay. We weaved and stumbled across the car park from the boat to the minibus, some clutching their belongings, others clutching each other. Simon was last on board the bus, helped by Pam.

Back on the minibus the mood was subdued, but not in a good way. Heads lolled from side to side or towards the knees and the red faces turned grey as outside the dusk fell. Sitting in the front passenger seat like a scout leader, my brain was beginning to foresee an approaching scenario. We had agreed that our party should be collected by loved ones at the company's leisure centre later that evening. Between 7.00 and 8.00pm, it would be busy and not the best place from which to disgorge our complement. Tipsy would be okay, comatose might not. Leaving with a group of mild-mannered office workers in the morning and retuning with stragglers from the zombie apocalypse the same evening would not reflect well. To our credit, we had shown a fair degree of resilience. The food had been paltry and the mixers had run out in the early afternoon, so everyone had been subsisting on neat spirits ever since. However, this would never stand as an excuse, so I resolved to improve the odds.

The minibus was twenty-five minutes away from King's Lynn. Along the ring road we would be passing an Asda superstore, offering a good place for a pit stop, whilst providing me with the opportunity to buy a mountain of crisps and snacks to act as blotting paper for the alcohol. Supplemented by gallons of bottled water and juices, we might be able to use the bus as a travelling recovery ward for the last hour or so of the journey. Perhaps, like a wilted bunch of flowers, this might be enough to revive us? Twenty minutes out from King's Lynn a message travelled up the bus that Simon needed the toilet. I asked him to hold on, as there were no known alternatives ahead. Ten minutes later the message was passed again, but we were now eating up the dual carriageway on the approach to the town which glowed orange in the distance ahead of us, so I sent back the same response. After the exit slip road, we slowly negotiated the traffic lights on a tortuous three-lane roundabout and took the turning into the semi-darkness of the half empty supermarket car park. As soon as we came to rest and the hand brake was pulled, I jumped out and jogged up to the entrance snatching a vacant trolley en route, rattling it under the canopy and through the automatic doors where I paused to pick out the hanging sign for the crisps and confectionery aisle. A single slow pass between the shelves was all that was needed to part fill the trolley with large multi-bags of crisps and snacks. Next, the trolley's front compartment was filled to capacity from the soft drinks aisle. There was no queueing at the checkout, so after a swipe of the company credit card I was back at the minibus a few moments after, offering one of those expressions given by someone who is about to hand out comfort and charity. This was returned by a cluster of worried faces.

"Everything alright?" I said.

"Simon's had a fall," was the collective response.

I'm not sure if it has been discovered by science or not, but we each contain some kind of special juice in the form of neuro-transmitter or a hormone or an enzyme or something that can sober a drunk in an instant. Science might also one-day conclude that it works faster when one is blaspheming and uttering expletives. Whatever the chemical messenger, it surged through in the split second that I was coming to terms with the words "Simon's had a fall". Looking around the nearby gloom and then craning to stare into the minibus, there was no evidence of an ongoing medical emergency.

"What happened and where is he?" was the best that I could come up with.

"Well," started Pam,

"the moment the minibus stopped, he reached back for the handle, swung a back door open and then bailed out backwards - like a frogman off a rubber dingy".

"Then he pulled himself up, grabbed his stick and made off as if we'd entered him into the Paralympics," came a voice from someone else.

"He's in the gents' toilets and Mark is looking after him."

"Oh fuck a duck," I muttered, turning back toward the supermarket.

The toilets were to the right of the entrance beyond the checkouts and the customer service kiosk. Inside, Mark was facing the only toilet cubicle of the four that was closed, talking in a soothing voice to the powder blue laminate door in attempt to persuade Simon into opening it. I made my presence known with an awkward knock and a concerned greeting but got no response. Mark and I retired to the sinks.

"Is he okay, is he injured?" I whispered to Mark.

"He is conscious, and he says that he's okay, but is refusing to come out," was the response.

We both tried a little tag team coaxing for a minute or two, but it was getting us nowhere, so I attempted the louder, formal voice and told him to open the door right away, or we would have to force it. There was a pause, then some tapping from the other side of the partition as the walking stick prodded the door and was used to push the bolt aside, so that it swung inwards a foot. Mark reached forward and peered in with compassion. As a grey-haired man of a similar age to Simon, it was a relief to see him take charge. Inside was not a pretty sight. On the plus side, there was no blood, but Simon was sitting, bedraggled on the toilet with his pants and trousers around his ankles in a puddle of his own making.

Mark examined a bump on the back of Simon's head, which did not appear alarming and then moved on to assess the wider situation whilst offering reassuring comments about getting everything cleaned up and being on our way. I stood like a lemon, averting my eyes, listening to the shufflings in the cubicle and passing in occasional extra toilet roll. After some rattling of a belt, Mark came out of

109

the cubicle seeking another conference at the sinks. His conclusion was that the pants and trousers were soaked beyond saving through any amount of dabbing.

Wound tight with nervous energy an opportunity flashed. The superstore was large enough to have a small clothing section, so I could solve the problem by speed-buying some trousers and could get out of the uncomfortable situation in the toilet. So, I sped out only to return three seconds later to ask Simon through the cubicle about his waist size.

"I'm thirty-eight inches," came in the subdued response. Under the dimmer light of the clothing area it wasn't hard to find a pair of black standard issue trousers in size thirty-eight. The supermarket was near empty and most of the staff at the checkout seemed aware that there was an incident-in-progress because they kept peering towards the toilets as I paid for the trousers with cash, refusing the offer of a receipt to save a couple of seconds. On return, Mark had made preparations by removing Simon's shoes and lower garments. Taking the trousers from me, he went into the cubicle where Simon was sitting on the pan and deftly started to feed a leg into the trousers. The second leg was pressed into service so that in quick succession both feet protruded. What happened next is seared into my memory. The toilet had that clammy quality of a gym changing room and to make matters worse, the subject to be dressed was still a fraction damp, so the trousers would go to the knees, but they would go no further. I had moved over and deposited the older trousers and underwear in the bin and was already wincing at the unsavoury scene in the cubicle ahead of me, before Mark found it necessary to ask Simon to stand up to ease the progress of his trousers, as he himself moved down onto his knees to get better purchase on the waistband.

As if they had been waiting for a cue in an English farce, behind me the main door swung open and in stepped a father, ushering his ten-year-old son by the shoulder. He stood frozen for a second, bathed in surprise with the door closing slowly behind them and then banging shut.

As his on-board computer tried but failed to decipher the information coming in through his eyes, his facial expression changed to dumbfounded and then tightened into disgust. The possibility that he and his junior charge might have stepped through a wormhole into the toilets on fetish-night in a Berlin gay club, is a scenario unlikely to have registered. However, the sight of a twenty-eight-year-old man staring nervously into a toilet cubicle, where a second, grey-haired man was kneeling, facing a tousle-haired senior citizen on a walking stick - who was standing, naked from the waist down and being tugged at so furiously that his glasses were wonky - could have put the Berlin option right into the running. Meanwhile, unaware of his new audience, Mark continued pulling and grunting at Simon's midriff. An audible straining from Mark and a simultaneous groan from Simon signalled to me, but not to the other onlookers, that the trousers had negotiated the hips. Exhausted, Simon looked out in grim-faced apology. Rendered similarly catatonic, I also stood there dumbly, unable to offer an excuse or a bon mot to lighten the moment.

With marvellous, subconscious dexterity our visitor moved his palm from the shoulder to the crown of his son's head and then twisted his wrist with the result that the boy spun around abruptly to face the door again. Turning himself by ninety degrees, so that he did not take his eyes off the degenerates before him for a nanosecond, he pushed against the force of the door-closer and bundled his junior and then

111

himself back out into the reassuring world of piped music and respectable shoppers.

Now terrified that this situation might repeat itself, I finally stepped forward to get my hands dirty in the cubicle. Despite the victory in getting the trousers over the hips to waist height, it transpired that the war was not yet won. There was a large v-shaped aperture at the front that remained wide open, signalling to me that the Battle of the Bulge was about to begin. On Mark's command, I reached around him and got a firm grip on both sides of Simon's new waistband, so there was a little slack to work with. As a result, Mark managed to engineer the zip a third of the way up its track before it stopped, due to the growing sideward forces. Even asking Simon to breathe in only bought us another inch of zip, with the trouser buttons remaining far apart either side. Mark twisted his head to me, so that we were now almost kissing and asked,

"Are these really a thirty-eight?"

"Yes they are," I responded, a little defensively, whilst bending my own head forward to reread the tag stapled to the waistband… which fortunately confirmed a thirty-eight. Then drawing himself back a little to look up at Simon, Mark asked,

"Are you really a thirty-eight?"

Looking down, Simon paused abjectly, before his face crumpled.

"I'm a forty-four," came the mumbled response followed by a sniff.

"Why didn't you say?" Mark enquired calmly and almost rhetorically.

"I didn't want you to know," came the wretched response. A moment of melancholy was about to envelop us, which I managed to bat away by inadvertently uttering the words,

"Oh you bastard," only to receive a stern reproach from Mark, who had already started removing the trousers. Once off, he handed them back to me.

"Right!" I said indignantly,

"I'll go and see to these then".

Picking up a new pair of forty-four-inch trousers from the clothes section took no more than sixty seconds, but I paused and drew breath when nearing the checkouts, opting to divert to the customer service desk, catching the eye of the matronly manager on approach. With an unconvincing smile I placed an exceedingly crumpled, floor stained and soiled looking pair of trousers on the counter and then handed over the new ones on their hanger saying,

"I'd like to change these trousers please."

With just a finger and thumb, she lifted them up a little from the counter and raised her eyes to mine as she furrowed her brow.

In life, attack can occasionally be the best form of defence, so before she had summoned thoughts on how to remonstrate, I was out of the traps.

"Look, I don't have a receipt, but I bought these here only ten minutes ago from checkout nine - and before you say anything else, please know that there is a half-naked, disabled man in your gents' toilet who is in urgent need of *this* pair of trousers."

Hearing the strain in my voice and realising that any other course of action would involve a very public meltdown from the jittery customer in front of her, the manager accepted the return by pushing the size thirty-eight trousers into the under-counter bin with an elbow. She then scanned the new trousers and suggested that I get on with my mission.

Round two of fitting the trousers was a simpler, less muscular activity. A six-inch addition to the girth meant that they slipped on without effort. With just a few moments in front of the mirror at the sink, Simon made himself presentable, at which point I went ahead to gather the rest of the crew so that the minibus was ready to depart the moment he hobbled on board. An hour later we had reached our final destination.

Although most were a little slurred and others were already suffering from early onset hangovers, the handover to husbands, wives and partners was civilised enough. A handful insisted on going in for a couple of drinks in the leisure club, but I declined on the grounds of fatigue, but in truth no amount of alcohol could make me unwind from, or un-see one particular aspect of the day. Waiting outside we made small-talk with Simon as his taxi arrived and then we bade him goodnight. He had partially recovered from the brandy overdose and appeared to be in good enough spirits as we waved him off. Collapsing into bed that night, I hoped that the incident might be quietly buried in the 'what goes on tour, stays on tour' vein.

The next morning, however, Simon's workspace remained empty as the clock moved through nine to ten to eleven. We made enquiries at the sheltered accommodation where he lived. The warden explained that Simon had arrived home safely, but had then taken a second taxi to hospital because he was feeling unwell. I had my suspicions that just like me at the Asda customer service desk the previous evening, Simon was getting his retaliation in first. Like the wily corporate chess player that he was, he was improving his starting point for the inevitable series of meetings with the union and HR that would now surely follow.

The big question that you may already have asked is - can it be appropriate to recount such a tale when it is about a disabled person? It's a very fair thought that I've also pondered. On one side there is a story about a vulnerable man in even more vulnerable circumstances and it could be argued that to tell such a story is bad taste. Nearly everybody misbehaved on the work outing, but it was only Simon who paid a high price. As if things were not bad enough, and to make matters worse, he became the butt of this off-colour story too.

Conversely, one might also say that anyone who drinks half a bottle of brandy on an empty stomach in the mid-afternoon is cruising for a bruising - disabled or not. Friends often say to me, "go on, have a few drinks and enjoy yourself," or "what's the worst thing that could happen if we have a couple more?" I'm tempted, but something in particular from the distant past stirs, accompanied by the faintest whiff of a supermarket toilet. In re-telling this story again, there is no intention to besmirch the memory of a former colleague. The reason is to expand on a concept that was penned by Henry James Thoreau. He wrote:

"Things do not change. We change".

The tale of Simon in the supermarket toilet may have remained unedited in my head if events in my life had not unfolded as they have. Perhaps it is the big man upstairs who is having the last laugh, because now I can really, fully appreciate the tragedy that sits alongside the farcical scene in the toilet.

Sitting here typing, all I have to do is to lift my head to look up from the laptop screen and I'm the one in the cubicle, with my trousers in a puddle of urine around my ankles, staring outwards, but unable to meet the eyes of my helpers. The embarrassment, the shame, the helplessness swirl together so potently that the urge to leap up, lash out and sprint away can't be supressed, but the body simply won't respond even to this most desperate of mental commands, so the anguish amplifies around the walls of the cubicle and turns to despair.

28 Days in Kerala (Extracts)

A few years ago now, a chain of meandering coincidences took me on a journey to South India, where a bustling hospital - which is part detention centre, part spa and part asylum - cares for people from every corner of the globe. There, I had twenty-eight days of relentless treatments based on a 3000-year-old recipe. The endless array of bizarre treatments was so bewildering that I scribbled a journal down on napkins and receipts at the end of each day, as a form of therapy.

28 Days in Kerala recounts these days and it scratches the surface of the magic and absurdity of living, of illness and of healing. The fact that the AVS hospital in Kottakkal is teeming with patients and staff is perhaps not so surprising. We all know that some people will go to great lengths when challenged by illness. One would therefore expect the patients to be either gullible or desperate, but to the contrary, I found the near opposite. Although almost always colourful to a very ordinary and drab Englishman, many of the other inmates were also scientists of one kind or another or were medically trained. A common theme was that the majority of patients were castoffs from Western medicine. They had tried everything available in shiny hospitals or had been told that their condition is untreatable. Using traditional Ayurvedic Medicine, the AVS Hospital dares to

117

heal the seriously afflicted. Somehow it often does. In writing a book, I hoped to capture the life stories and healing journeys of a few of the unusual types of people whose paths I crossed during the hot and humid stay on the sixth floor.

Part of the month-long regime, called the 'Panchakarma' involves enemas. Although it is childish, this is a natural source of material which is almost guaranteed to entertain anyone from Great Britain. In compiling these extracts, there is no wish to leave the reader with the sense that the world-renowned AVS Hospital is just an enema factory in a fois-gras sense, but…up-the-bottom action, well that's just funny isn't it.

A chance meeting in hospital with some old friends led to contact with a man who had inexplicably turned his own neurological health around in unusual circumstances. We spoke on the phone and then I read his book about a trip to a curious hospital in India. Whilst mulling this over, I had also put out feelers to find anyone with my condition who had survived for a long period. By fluke, a friend's neighbour knew someone in the nearby town. We met and discussed the strategies that she had employed. The list was very short. Annie's mainstay was that for six years in a row, she had spent one month of each year receiving treatment in a hospital in India. I sat across the table in the coffee shop agog. Annie was describing, at first hand, the same treatments at the same hospital that I had just read about. On returning home, I searched out everything that I could about the Arya Vaidya Sala (AVS) hospital in Kerala, India.

118

By now summer had moved into autumn. To our surprise, the hospital's treatment regimes were inexpensive. The bad news was that the Arya Vaidya Sala had a moratorium in place. It was not taking any new patients, as it was booked solid for the next twenty-four months. Then, as autumn moved to winter, there came a call from Annie. She and her husband had decided that travelling to India was now beyond their capacity. This meant that room 602 in the hospital would be free in January. With a little sleight of hand and some diplomacy, I might just be able to jump the queue.

22nd January 2015 (Thursday)

The month, in fact the New Year has built up towards today. Long lists of to-dos have been written in columns and most have been checked off. So far the winter is two-thirds through and it has not thrown out the spite and violence of last year's storms, or the icy chill two years prior to that. However, an unexpected dump of snow as the light faded on Boxing Day coincided with a squally, westerly wind and plummeting temperatures. The snow quickly iced, sticking fast to branches, dragging tree limbs to the ground, splitting conifers in the old garden in halves or quarters as their trunks separated. Removed by chainsaws, the garden lay dormant in the monochrome of January.

Leaving home had to be done with a matter-of-fact air about it. We would depart after dropping the children at school, whilst their grandma was already in transit, travelling northwards to take up the reins in anticipation of collecting them, so that the travellator of their childhood

119

lives continued unchecked, but under new escort. The transition would be seamless, undisruptive, without fuss. So the planning and packing had to be done with an air of calm and cheerfulness. Some of this was genuine, as a sense of adventure had begun to build to combat the dread and guilt associated with leaving children at home and in the cold for four weeks. By late morning, Charlie and I were delivered to Heathrow Terminal Four in our taxi driver Dorian's safe hands. We took one last look into the milky winter light, before the doors swooshed us into the terminal.

23rd January (Friday)

We are very fortunate to have Room 602, which we get into three hours later, after a light doze and our first tentative journey to the hospital canteen. In hotel terms Room 602 is one of the penthouse suites in the Centenary block of the hospital. This is the mid-market block preferred by many of the international visitors, ahead of the newer glass and steel Annex building that sits nearby and is apparently used mainly by wealthy Arabs, though I bet that even their fingers stick to the light switches. The two other blocks hold accommodation of varying standards ranging from small apartments for families to open wards.

The sixth floor corridor is brown tiled underfoot, with once white, but now nicotine-yellow tiles up the walls, separated by sturdy doors inset at regular intervals. The ceiling is low and there is no light save from a glow from the stairwell and a sun-dazzle from either end, which is enclosed with plate glass. The overall vibe is Pentonville Prison meets Tenko.

Our room is dimly lit, shaded, but airy with impressively high ceilings leading to a small enclosed corner balcony and kitchenette, or tiled cupboard with a sink. It looks onto the hospital's squat and broken down engineering building, sporting blue tarpaulins stretched across broken roofs. Beyond it is the steep hospital road running up into the town, that has been canalized by high walls and shop fronts pressing onto a thin band of occasional pavement. Across the road, a cluster of factory and office buildings whizz, whine and smoke day and night, making the medicines for this and the other four AVS sister hospitals, looking like a small, third world version of Willy Wonka's chocolate factory. Beyond that are palm trees and hillsides with scattered houses set in a jungle that stretches to the horizon.

31st January (Saturday)

My Charlie left this morning. I am bereft.

On the taxi ride back from the airport I watched the sun rising out of the clouds an inch from above the horizon as it does every day, owing to a trick of the light I do not understand. I gazed at the scenery. A mongoose ran into our path, but lost in thought, the rest of the journey ended where it started, at the gate of the AVS Hospital.

We had been up before 5.00am and were already waiting for our taxi driver, Rafeeque to arrive when he drove up. His assessment was that there was just enough time for me to come along to the airport and be dropped off again at the hospital for a 7.45am treatment. The tight deadline was the only encouragement that he wanted. He would be a go-to man if anyone anywhere needed a getaway driver. We sped through the darkness, overtaking all in sight with his headlights on full beam, sparring and jostling with fast moving, unladen trucks as they emerged through the soupy, diesel gloom.

In the short jungle stretches between villages, barefoot figures loomed out of the darkness, walking along the dust verges. As I stared out of the rectangle of the windscreen, it was part Rudyard Kipling and part Grand Theft Auto. The odd tuc-tuc sprang from a track with only its solitary moped light for illumination, forcing Rafeeque to take evasive action by pushing down on the accelerator and swerving.

At Calicut International Airport, Charlie and I said our tender goodbyes, and then she was gone, disappearing into the terminal with blue jeans and a wiggle of the hips. On returning, I made a mental note that it was time to man up for the three weeks ahead. The rest of the day passed like clockwork as the one that preceded it and the ones to follow. I'll summarise the routine, so as not to repeat it until the treatments change.

The day starts with the medicated ghee ordeal. To breakfast at 7.00am for porridge. Back to "T-up" the day: fetching water, arranging laundry, checking medication and provisions, changing into oil-stained clothing and laying out the plastic sheet. At 7.40am a man takes away the oil massage paraphernalia from a cupboard in the room. I think the same oil is used on me for the twenty-eight days (perhaps then it is suitably salt-seasoned for the canteen?). At 7.45am I am fetched for the oil-on-the-head-treatment and an hour of basting. On leaving, I am instructed to rest in bed for one hour. However, ten minutes later I am wrapped to the shoulders in olive tapenade and bandaged up with instructions to rest for two hours. These two hours are then interrupted every fifteen minutes as people shuttle in and out of the room on routine hospital business. At 11.40am the bandages are unwound and I shower hard for fifteen minutes in a vain attempt to remove the oil and debris. 12.00 noon is lunch in the canteen, before the more sociable people arrive. 12.30 to 1.45pm is set aside for errands and e-mails and then back into oily clothes.

At 1.40pm the man comes to get the rice pudding rub-a-dub kit from the room and leads me away. After that, there is one further hour of lying on the bed in oil and dried rice pudding taking it to 4.15pm when more 'meds' are taken and I shower again in readiness to see the world or to run errands. Then, it's soup at 5.30pm, ready for yoga at 6.00 until 7.20pm and into the canteen for salad, fruit and strange encounters with the weird and wonderful. Finally, it is upstairs to the room at 8.30pm for appalling medical concoctions and to wait for the phone call from our little girls at 9.30pm. Soon after, it's bed, hoping that the din of the outside world will facilitate and not deter a night of sleep.

7th February (Saturday)

It was hot by 7.00am and I opened the balcony door for the day, switching off the squeaky AC en route. A week of enemas now looms. The sapping nature of this process forms the basis of many patient conversations. I hope that "E-day" might be postponed, with the doctor coming in and muttering something about unfavourable weather conditions or the movement of enemy panzer divisions. The time for the morning oil massage came and went, but I was then led away for just the oil-on-the-head treatment without the accompanying tag-team massage. This was disconcerting as I've been clinging to my routine here in a life that could easily come adrift without it.

The arms got bandaged very late with only thirty minutes from un-bandaging to eat lunch before the rice-pud massage. The doctors had mentioned yesterday that the rice massage was going to change, increasing from two to four masseurs. I'd thought nothing more of it, but on arriving in the cramped cell at the appointed hour I realised that nothing here should be taken for granted. There was a different atmosphere. A new team consisting of older, wilier looking men looked up at me as they tied their steaming bags of rice. As I stripped, a grey-haired man passed me a muslin thong giving me a look that said, "Okay sonny, let's see what you're made of". It was going to be a contest, and I sensed it would be a sticky one.
Right from the start they chose not to play fair. I hoisted myself onto the basting tray swinging my legs a little, in a show of defiance and was not surprised when a man came over with a small bowl of warm oil and tipped an eggcup full onto my head.
"Is that all you've got, old man?" I thought.

He smiled to reveal two large, lonely teeth in his top gum and then placed a rectangle of muslin on my head and folded it in two so that it covered my scalp. I began to feel unnerved. Next he took a long strap of white muslin and tied it, with the two rough tugs of a granny knot, exceedingly tightly around my forehead. Now in just a muslin thong and wearing something akin to a baby's bonnet I felt a shiver of concern as I lay back in the tray and closed my eyes. These guys were definitely not playing by the rules. The usual chatter was absent and just the extractor fan whirred as they set about their work. Each grabbed a limb and started rubbing vigorously with a rice bag. Immediately it was a disorientating experience. With just two masseurs the subconscious brain keeps track of roughly who is doing what. With four, all tugging limbs in different directions as they work, it cannot. It's a proper pummelling - the massage equivalent of getting a good shoeing outside a pub from four men, who happen to be wearing enormous fluffy slippers.

It's quite absurd. With my eyes closed I try not to conjure up a picture of what this scene looks like, but cannot, and end up biting on a grin. You could not make this stuff up. Terry Gilliam would struggle to better it for lunacy. Neither thoughts about the jungle outside nor my state of health are enough to block out the exquisite stupidity of the moment. I open my eyes a fraction to receive another toothy smile and let out an involuntary chuckle and then another. Things are heading towards a convulsion of laughter, that feeling one used to get at school, and I struggle to get a grip.

However, the physical sensation of it all begins to take over as the sensory nervous system is overwhelmed and the brain gives up trying to keep up. In seeking a parallel experience from which to navigate, my mind unearths a moment late in my childhood where I was roughly tumbled by a breaking wave and lay bobbing in the surf with dulled senses.

8th February (Sunday)

Nothing really happened today. E-day came and went again. Maybe it has been postponed again? Something about troop movements in the Pas-de-Calais and suspicious answers in The Daily Telegraph crossword? The hospital functions as it does every other day despite it being a Sunday. As an aside, in Kerala it's a six-day week. By mid afternoon I had begun to let my guard down and had mentally reduced the enema terror threat from imminent to just critical.

However, a man did pop in at 4.00pm, whimsically taking a foot-long comedy syringe out of a metal box as he arrived. He asked me to take my shorts down and lie on my side whilst he injected 150ml of oil up my bottom. He was gone seconds later, after explaining that I may have two 'idly' for breakfast or if I prefer, two slices of unbuttered toast before the 'Kashayam' enema, that would be at 11.30am tomorrow. There was also no need for medicated ghee (hooray) or to take medicines in the morning, which was also good. Then I realised with a shudder that anything taken by mouth would drop through me like a stone into a well. The doctor came after that and I tried to ask him what I should do now. Would the oil ooze out (explaining why the kiosk downstairs has a floor to ceiling stock of adult incontinence pads) or was the oil just put up there for safekeeping, owing to a glut in the canteen? We were unable to decipher each other's English, so I gave up and spent an hour in my room speaking with Charlie and the girls by phone without seepage. After which I went gingerly to the canteen, having made a mental note not to cough, stifle sneezes or to laugh. That night as I got into bed my waters broke.

9th February (Monday)

Enemas are great! As soon as I get home I'm going to pop out to Wilkinson's and buy a length of hose. I'll borrow the funnel from the balsamic vinegar bottle, attaching it to one end and commandeer the kettle for the other. Then I'll go out into the road and invite in two strangers, asking one of them to stick the pointy end up my bottom and the other to hoist and tip the kettle. All the while we will engage in small talk about Wayne Rooney and Test Cricket. I'll then clench my buttocks and knock-kneed will see them out, before rushing to spend an exhilarating hour or so on the toilet.
Nobody, I think, likes the thought of an enema. It is possible that men may be a fraction more fearful as our lower bodies are not designed to have equipment inserted internally. But apart from the nudity, embarrassment, discomfort, alarming new sensations and the ensuing sense of humiliation and shame, enemas are not so bad.

Before arriving here, I had made a trip over to the doctor's surgery in Stamford to see the nurse for a last-minute typhoid jab. The jab itself had taken two minutes, but the appointment had taken fifteen as the nurse read to me from a computer screen about the do's and don'ts when travelling in India. I yawned inwardly when the little lecture extended to not going out in the midday sun and keeping hydrated, thinking that if the nurse had her own way, she'd require me to wear swimming goggles, a set of overalls and to hold my breath for the duration of the trip. With a worried tone she quizzed me about staying in an Indian hospital. I confirmed that the NHS had kindly provided me with a set of hypodermic needles and catheters, which was half true, and that I would avail myself of them if anything more serious than a splinter occurred during my stay. She asked me to reconfirm that nothing invasive was going to happen to me at the hospital. This I did, but then stupidly added "other than the enemas". She recoiled and stared at my face as though a large arachnid had started crawling out of a nostril. I heard her brain whirr as she made a mental image of an Indian hospital enema and then whirr again as she tried to delete it. Even so, I noticed her hands contort slightly in disgusted reflex. If she could only have seen the events of earlier today, with me being enema-ed to within an inch of my life by two smiling, moustachioed Indian men, I'm certain she'd have taken the remainder of the day off to go home and lie down.

The enema came to me, rather than me to the enema. I had it in my room. I always thought that you went for an enema in the same way that one goes out for a curry or a haircut. As the two smiling Indian men busied themselves preparing their apparatus, the language barrier left me unable to make quips about which end they would be using, so my mind turned to possibilities of a mobile enema business in

England. What might a such a business be called? I settle on R.S. Irrigation Services, with the strap line 'No Job Too Large'. The Italian subsidiary would naturally be branded 'Innuendo'. Would you recruit staff from health clinics or just use plumbers' apprentices? Should the enema business be combined with another symbiotic activity as is done with tyres and brakes? If so, would it work best with ear syringing or window cleaning? What would people write with their fingers in the dirt on the back on the van? This chain of thought had too many loose ends, so to speak, so I gave up on it as soon as my eyes began to water.

17th February (Tuesday)

My body does not know if it is coming or going. It is definitely going though. The medicated ghee is now exiting apparently entirely unaltered by the digestive tract. I'm repulsed by this and initially think that it's possible that I'm now overflowing with the yellow gore. It could be just a precursor to major organ failure. This would be preferable to drowning in ghee. However, on reflection, our children's very first nappies were also of a sticky mustard consistency. Perhaps my stomach has been reborn? Whatever is going on down there is not a cocktail for a stable emotional state either, as I became teary during the rice massage today. The men didn't seem to notice or mind and continued to murmur across the table to each other, which suited me fine, as the odd tear fell away. Having rejected the idea of ten spoons of ghee first thing this morning, I decided on a small act of rebellion and ordered four slices of unbuttered toast for breakfast.

After being bandaged there was a knock on the door from Jabare, the Egyptian man from down the hall. He had come to enquire how I am and looks shocked by the bandaged man before him, but soon comes in and pulls up a chair. He asks if the treatment is working and I ask about his own. His damaged knees seem to be improving through a mixture of massage and leg wraps. I mention the week of enemas that had just passed. He looks perplexed, wrinkling his unshaved face and asks in broken English to explain, "What is enema?"

I do my best, in words of few syllables as his eyes widen. After emitting a long,

"Aaaah," he pauses for a second, but his face then wrinkles to show that he thinks he might have misunderstood and then makes a mime of an injection into the stomach. I go for a more elaborate explanation of an enema and he seems dumbfounded for a second and half whispers to me in a hiss with inflection,

"In zee asss?!"

I nod slowly as he double-checks for confirmation. A large smile breaks out across his face as a chuckle erupts. He looks at me as if we have just shared a dirty secret and says, "Really, in zee asss!"

He's not sleeping well either. Sharing a room with his four-year-old son and wife is not the problem. Pointing to the room he explains that he grew up in a similar space with his parents, three brothers and one sister. He talks of his busy mind. As financial controller of one of Egypt's retailers he has a lot on, but his chief concern is that by neglecting his health and playing football on bad knees against his doctor's advice, he has done damage to his own mobility and therefore to his family's future. What's more, life is now much more complicated than before.

"My thizinking goes like sizz," he says.

When he was a boy, he only had one pencil to do his homework and drawings with. He'd nurture the pencil, writing and sharpening it with great care. When it was too short, he'd find an old pen lid on the street to use as a pencil extension and write with it until there was no lead. Now he says, his son has dozens of pencils that are accidentally stepped on when left scattered on the floor of their large Cairo apartment. His poorer childhood life was uncomplicated, but now his richer adult life is very complicated and therefore stressful. Stories like this are told the world over, with old-timers back home offering their own about books, screws, nails, apples and oranges. Abundance does not guarantee happiness, we all know that, but as he goes on, his story parts from my usual frame of understanding. He asks if I had heard of the troubles in Egypt? I nod saying that we'd followed the events closely at home on the TV and in the press. He looks pleased, but then goes on to say that it would be better if the period of unrest was known as the Arab Autumn and not Arab Spring.

Sleeping badly started for him during the uprising, with fear for the safety of his family and friends. His company's headquarters, near to Tahrir Square was first looted and then burned. For months every time he turned on a computer or TV screen anywhere, he'd have a flash of the smashed and smouldering equipment in his office. As a secular businessman, without strong religious or political affiliation to the revolutionaries or to the State, he felt vulnerable to everything and everyone during and after the uprising. But he says he's been training his mind since and

131

with regular mental effort, has weaned himself off the sense of defencelessness and fear, replacing them at every junction with something more positive. However, coming here has caused a relapse. Perhaps he's also a victim of the curse of being wrapped in bandages and told to relax by ever-smiling doctors?

Two days later, I'm accosted again by Jabare in the corridor, carrying a laptop with his hair short cropped and his face clean shaven. He takes me to one side seeking privacy.
"Now I have enema," he says with a mix of excitement and alarm, as if we share a special bond.

19th February (Thursday)

The final day here has needed some organisational and mental preparation. Firstly, there is the administrative process for settling the account, which is likely to be byzantine. Second is the tipping and third is saying goodbyes. The fourth is grasping the medicine and lifestyle routine that I'm expected to take back home to England. Lunch today was with an older couple who were Indian of heritage, but from Calgary via Tanzania. At this time of year it can drop to minus fifty with wind chill. I assume that it was Calgary and not Tanzania they were talking about. Although it's been eye-opening chatting with people from every part of the globe this past month and the topics have been illuminating, I'm tiring of it all and look forward to getting home and having a good old British whinge with drab looking people like me.

One thing that has surprised me as I begin to reflect, is the number of scientists here. There are more of them than I could have possibly imagined. By scientists, I mean the type of scientifically trained people who I thought would shun a place that offers up herbs and rubbing to combat cancers, disease and organ failure. By day four we had met a water scientist, engineers, a cancer and a brain researcher, a chemist, a pharmacologist, a lung specialist and others who should know better. On speaking with a couple called Renu and Chino, a pharmacist and public health specialist, at dinner on the fourth night, I mentioned how struck by this we had been. As scientists themselves, they were not. Renu commented without blinking, that scientists better understand the boundaries of science and therefore appreciate just how much is not understood by science and medicine. For them, knowing how little is understood can be a locus to seek out alternative treatments. In other words, just because science has not figured out how and why a therapy works, it does not automatically render the therapy ineffective. Acupuncture and Reiki are now fairly regularly used in hospitals, but as far as I know nobody has the foggiest scientific idea of what a meridian is or how it might work.

If Indian bureaucracy is a hangover from the British Raj, then this afternoon's experience in settling the hospital account is all our fault. This makes it no less painful. Since the moment of our arrival twenty-eight days ago, every single event at the hospital has involved someone thrusting a receipt into my hand. Every massage, every piece of equipment, each box of medicines, every concoction - be it by mouth or bottom - all meals, yoga sessions, doctors' visits, laundry and cleaning are accompanied by a receipt.

133

Most are large flimsy bits of paper sporting dot-matrix print from a computer roll. Others are the top wafer of the triplicate sheet from a receipt book. At first I made an indiscriminate pile of bills in a corner, but as it began to topple, I re-sorted this dump pile by a 'receipt type' along the countertop in the room. However, if the cleaning happened whilst I was out on a massage, the cleaning man would mop the floor and to facilitate speedy drying, switch the ceiling fan to the jet-propeller setting as he left. On returning to the room I'd find a portion of the receipts fluttering in suspension in their own dust devil, as if I'd walked into a classroom at Hogwarts. The remaining receipts would be evenly distributed about the floor.

On the last day I gathered every receipt and dumped them by the armful onto the metal tray table that straddled the bed for a memento photograph. The table soon overflowed, as all together the receipts would have filled my suitcase. A caustic and bony woman from Belgium had advised, early on, for me to follow her example and keep a running tally of all expenditure. Her experience was that this saved her some Rupees when she negotiated her final bill, but I had already pigeonholed her as being wizened, mean and most likely a trouble maker and had not taken the advice.

This was a good decision, because after an hour of settling the account in the hospital administration building, whilst the AC fought and lost its battle to keep the afternoon heat from rising, I would have handed over my credit card, paid any sum of money and possibly signed over the deeds to our home, just to make the ordeal stop. I paid the bills without even exploring the reams of paper beneath each sub-total, then made a mental note to return after dark with a petrol bomb.

Innocent Lives (Extracts)

Sequential readers will already be acquainted with my grand-parents, Mamie and Pépé. Paulette & Dédé (their christian names) were both orphaned in their teens and each was left in charge of their younger siblings. They were united in something close to an arranged marriage with the whole band, numbering seven, moving into Mamie's parents' four roomed house at 6 Rue Pierre Fournier, Lamotte-Beuvron in La Sologne, France. Life was already tough, even before the second world war hit them like a tsunami, bringing four years of brutal Nazi occupation in its wake. Lamotte-Beuvron is in a little-known, forested area dotted with thousands of shallow, peaty lakes, but it is within striking distance of the cities of Tours, Orléans and Paris. During the war, this peaceful backwater became a place of refuge and resistance.

I wrote Innocent Lives as an account of the war as it happened in Lamottte, but also to retell the events of Mum's birth. She was born during the early hours of the 27th of August 1944. Later the same day Paris would be liberated. However, across La Sologne columns of vengeful German occupiers were in full retreat and chaos reigned.

The war and by definition the occupying Germans had robbed Paulette & Dédé of what should have been the best years of their lives and replaced these years with fear and danger. Save for a few loose comments, the plaques, the annual ceremonies - lest we forget - and the memorials, one might believe that the war never happened. Like any town or village across Britain there is a large monument by the town hall in Lamotte commemorating the fallen, but much more unnerving is stumbling across a memorial on a woodland path amongst the purple heather and chlorophyll bracken marking the spot of a tragedy. These are dotted across La Sologne. Hanging on a hook above other discarded detritus in my Uncle Daniel's open sided warehouse is one of only three pieces of physical proof of the war that I've ever seen. It's the rusting helmet of a German storm trooper pulled out of the ground in the forest by my uncle's digger.

One cold afternoon back in 2011, when I was trawling the internet for information about the occupation of La Sologne as the wood burner crackled and hissed in the background, my eyes were drawn to an unusual link in English to the National Holocaust Museum in New York. It contained the words Lamotte-Beuvron which I found unsettling enough to pause and re-read before clicking through. A dense archive page opened up with lists of places and dates. I scanned the tiny text before my eyes rested on a single line, "The sanatorium in Lamotte-Beuvron known as Les Pins was used as an internment camp for Jews during the war". That was it.

My mind wheeled back to a moment of time in 1991. As a young man, I had been working in Paris and roughly every two weeks would take the train and visit my grandparents to enjoy a weekend of Mamie's good cooking. They were fine company despite their near constant bickering and seemingly happy to see me come and go as I pleased, as long as I made it back to the Rue Pierre Fournier by seven to share an aperitif with Pépé. My grandparents quite often had company and on arriving back late in the afternoon one Saturday, I found them ensconced in their iron veranda with two friends of similar ages and eagerly accepted a Ricard with water. Whilst they talked amicably, I swapped a respectful greeting with a tiny older lady who was sitting quietly in the corner - as if placed there for safekeeping. The air outside was heavy and soon a stiff breeze announced the arrival of a weather front coming in from the south west making the open metal veranda doors rattle on their clasps. As the wind dropped and the first heavy spots of rain began to tap on the safety glass of the roof, we retreated into the humidity of the kitchen, where the shutters of the single window remained half closed. The room was lit only by the trio of bare bulbs that hung from the ceiling fan above the round table. We brought up the chairs and shuffled back into position, the diminutive old lady now to my left nursing her glass of vin douce. I zoned out as the cordial chatting continued, more interested in the flashes of lightning outside and unwilling to decipher the conversation against a radio show that prattled in the background. My neighbour was also distracted but tense, her head cocked back intently in concentration listening to the radio. I watched out of the corner of my eye as she became agitated, her hands and jaw moving erratically

137

possibly in the spasm of old age. Noticing the same her son reached his hand to hers, saying,

"Calme-toi Maman," in a gentle tone.

She pulled her hand away and thrust her head forward. "Non," she said defiantly,

"Call that man, get him on the phone, I want you to talk to him." The voice was hoarse and it rang with age and anguish.

"Call the man on the radio," she demanded.

Panicked, I switched attention to the radio. It was a phone-in show from the Orléans radio station about the surge in support for the National Front in forthcoming elections. In my reverie I had missed a change in direction as contributors had phoned in to question the extent or even the existence of the Holocaust. Electricity filled the gloom as we all listened eyes-down to the radio.

"Call him," the old lady implored again. There was a pause, again laced with pain.

"Tell him I was there, tell him that I saw everything, tell him that I lost everyone," but her son placed his hand on her shoulder whilst someone turned off the radio. We sat in uncomfortable silence. Then she tugged at her sleeve with a shaking hand and placed her forearm on the table where I sat. I stared down at the near translucent age freckled skin. On the inside of her wrist, blotted by time, was a single line of blue-black digits crudely tattooed into her skin.

Fixing her gaze on me she asked,

"Do you know what this is?"

This haunting tattoo of a Nazi concentration camp is the second piece of physical evidence that a terrible war came to the small, backwater town where my family lived.

On the corner of the Rue Pierre Fournier, a tidy two-storey house faces out to the Rue des Michalons, its narrow back vegetable garden tracking the pavement with a long row of hanging plum tomatoes growing temptingly close to the fence. Jean Le Page and his wife moved there in the mid-nineties. Unusually they'd moved from the coast in their retirement to a place that's about as far from the sea in France as can be. Jean was an avuncular man. As a neighbour, he lifted the spirits of my usually misanthropic grandpa. As a couple, they also softened the persistent squabbling between Mamie and Pépé, so their company was welcomed when they popped along for an aperitif. Jean was strong, white haired, in his sixties and of the joke-telling and back-slapping type. He was also straightforward and sincere. A joiner by trade, he had set up a workshop in the narrow run of outbuildings behind his home which he was keen to show off. So one summer evening we made our way to their house for the evening ritual. We started on Ricard whilst Monsieur Le Page showed me antique furniture they had brought up from Normandy and cabinets that he had made himself. I followed him to the small net-curtained dining room where he hunted for a bottle of Calvados which he promised had the power to cure all ills, whilst adding hair to the chest. I asked him where in Normandy he had come from, a dumb question as I've never been there, and he mentioned the name of a small village I hadn't heard of, which might have had Sur-Mer hyphenated to it - despite being a kilometre inland. Placing a big-fingered hand on my shoulder, he said,
"You look a lot like the first American soldier that I set eyes on in June of '44".
He went back to searching for his bottle whilst I pondered the level of disappointment one might feel in finding a

139

version of me as a liberator. When he returned to eye level, bottle in hand, his eyes appeared moist - though I thought little of it at the time. On re-joining the kitchen table and pouring shot glasses of illicit Calvados, which went down like apple aftershave, he picked up this theme again.

His parents had pulled him and his sisters down into their basement in the early hours of the 6th June as the D-Day air-raids had commenced with thuds and shudders. The previous afternoon had been tense with German troops travelling the coast road at speed and local rumour spreading in the evening that paratroopers had landed. His parents had been nervous. Unbeknown to the famille Le Page, the aerial bombing of the coastal batteries and reserve positions was just the beginning.

At 5.00am the biggest armada that had ever sailed unleashed the most ferocious naval bombardment in history. Even at ten years old, huddled in their groaning basement clinging to his family, Jean was certain that death would come or perhaps that the world itself would end. Then the fighting started. In fear the family spent two days and nights without light in the basement emerging on the morning of the 8th June to find a moonscape populated by Americans. They had lost many friends in the tumult. Gratitude for liberation here was not as it was portrayed in the Pathé newsreels of the day showing beautiful young women jumping onto tanks to kiss the GIs whilst café owners distributed wine. Here, it mingled with confusion, bitterness and loss. It's thought that 20,000 Norman civilians died on D-day and in the days soon after. To put it in context 43,000 British civilians died in the eight months of the Blitz. However, for a ten-year-old boy like Jean it was also an adventure.

In the end Monsieur and Madame Le Page moved back to Normandy, for reasons I do not know, leaving a hole in my grandparents' world. He left something for me with Mamie for our arrival on holiday the following summer. Wrapped in a piece of tissue paper and about the size of a cigarette lighter was a small brass object. We passed it around the veranda as we each guessed what it might be. It was the size of a large set of toenail clippers, but without any jaws. We asked if it was an old tool or gauge for joinery making? On pressing the thumb-press it made a pleasing and distinctive metallic click-clunk. Curiously it had the letters ACME embossed into it, the same letters painted on the equipment Wile E. Coyote would conjure up to do away with Road-Runner in the old cartoons. This was the clue to it being American and not Norman. It was what was nicknamed a "cricket" by American soldiers and issued to the paratroopers who were dropped at night behind enemy lines as a crude way of telling friend from foe in the tight-packed Normandy countryside. This small object, itself the cousin of a nineteen-thirties children's toy, is the third piece of evidence that I have of the war and it is strangely evocative. I keep it in a small wooden box by my bedside.

As night began on the evening of the 26th August 1944, everyone in Lamotte, rich or poor and without exception was already at home with doors bolted. The German curfew was of course no longer in force. Bands of FTP and Maquis resistors had now re-erected check points at either end of the town and by day were hiding their nerves as they listened for any information about local German troop movements. By night even they sought shelter. Hated though it was, the curfew had been replaced by something worse. The new self-imposed curfew came as darkness fell and night-fear swelled. Even the rear shutters which normally stayed open in the heat of summer were now closed, their latches snapped shut. The daytime sun still radiated through the stone bringing beads of sweat to the skin as people talked in low voices. Behind the shutters, men and women sat close to the open windows, hoping to feel a breeze and strained their ears for any signs of danger. Save for barking dogs and the ringing of the cicadas the town was growing dark and silent as the moon began its rise. People went to bed early, but slept fitfully in the heat. This afternoon Paulette had carried on despite her advanced pregnancy. She was feeling a tightening in her abdomen which she at first put down to the anxieties of recent days catching up with her. It was normal Paulette told herself and what's more she was not yet due, so she went to lie down to try to relax as soon as she had set the food on the table.

Soon she realised that the squeezing was now a regular pulse and had become contractions. The baby was coming. A wave of despair swept Dédé. A man caught outside tonight would be in great peril. The once bucolically calm streets of the town were a wild west where a guerrilla war played out alongside banditry and the settling of old scores. The Gendarmes were also cowering in their homes or barricaded into their station house. If spotted, Dédé would be shot either by roaming Germans or a wary resister without hesitation. There was no knowing if he would round the corner onto the main road to find another line of German trucks. They waited, hoping for a false alarm as the rest of the household began sensing the danger in turn, but the baby was coming and no cork nor war was going to stop it. Dédé needed to act. He would have to go out and get the midwife.

The shrinking glow of the sun could still be seen in the far west as he put his hands to the glass and peeked out. Taking a breath he put on his cap and crept out of the house into the hot dusky night air, pausing to look left and right as with both hands he moved the rusty gate open and stole out into the road, watching his long shadow on the dark silver street ahead of him. He moved first away from the town towards Les Pins, then cut along an alley to the Rue Pasteur walking softly from heel to toe on the grit, cursing that there was not enough darkness anywhere to envelop him. He kept close to the fences and felt the heat from the buildings as he passed. He paused again at the end of the road scouring up and down the Rue des Michalons for movement and seeing none. He exhaled looking up at the early stars in the blue-black sky, but also sensed the tension that hung heavy on the electrical wires over the street. Walking softy but briskly, Dédé made it through the light camouflage of shadows to the corner of the Route Nationale. His heart quickened as the unfamiliar smell of concrete dust and ash drifted on the air from the bombed-out railway station. Glancing all around he turned left, skimming his fingers along the brickwork of the corner house before retreating into the darkness of its doorway. From there he watched and listened, first straight ahead and then by leaning his head forward along wider arcs up and down the broad main road. No human nor animal prowled. No lights from the station, the maisons bourgeoises or the grand Hotel Tatin washed the pavements. Above the shops nothing stirred. He was inside one of his dreams as the only man left on Earth. For a moment he had an urge to walk out

143

and shout something at the top of his voice, to see if it echoed back to him. The still moonlit night now felt less threatening. There was no one to be afraid of, so Dédé stepped out onto the pavement and softly walked up the road to the squat terraced house of Madame Agan the midwife, whose doorway faced onto the street. He reversed into the shadows again looking straight ahead first and then peering out from left to right. After a pause, he rapped tentatively on the door and then again seeking a note of urgency, but without threat. The house remained silent. He knocked again a little harder and insistently, but looking up at the fanlight above the door it remained mole black. He went around to the front window and picking up a stone, tapped against the shutter, wincing at the metallic noise. A glow appeared in the fanlight. He returned to the door and in a whisper said,

"Madame Agan it's Dédé, I mean André Barbou, are you there? The baby is coming, we need your help".

The bolts on the door scraped from the inside and the lock turned. Madame Agan half opened it and Dédé slipped in. Standing in the hallway in her nightgown, her hair plaited, Madame Agan's normally plump face appeared ghostly as she looked at him from above her low-lit paraffin lamp. With a pained expression she ushered the young man into her kitchen where they remained standing as she lengthened the wick a touch. She asked Dédé for information. He gave it and she looked down for a moment in thought.

"With Paulette being so young and strong, there is a very good chance that the labour will be long."

Dédé nodded like a schoolboy and she continued,

"I will come first thing in the morning".

"But the baby *is* coming" he said raising his voice a little.

"I can't come tonight," responded Madame Agan unable to meet his eye.

"But we need you Madame Agan."

The stairwell to the side of the kitchen creaked under the bare feet of Monsieur Agan as he made his way to the kitchen with the braces of his trousers pulled up over an untucked shirt. He nodded to Dédé.

"She's not coming," he said in a firm tone. "I won't let her go out tonight."

"But she has a pass said Dédé feebly." Monsieur Agan shook his head a little and then put a hand on Dédé's shoulder.

"Go home," he said. "If it is safe, she will come in the morning."

Madame Agan ushered Dédé back to the hallway taking care to extinguish her lamp. They stood in the semi darkness as she offered advice and instructions to Dédé, but he was now elsewhere. As the door closed behind him and the bolts slipped again, his dazed thoughts turned to despair. It was a feeling that he recognized well, but this time it engulfed him. He turned back into the road biting his lip as he looked around. Still nothing. After a few paces he stopped still thinking that he could hear the noise of an engine over his thoughts, but it was his mind playing tricks. The moon had now risen and the stars had multiplied. He had failed. He was nothing. They were all nothing. God had treated them with contempt again.

At the Rue des Michalons he didn't bother to stop and look ahead, walking blindly whilst his stomach gnawed at him. On passing through the shadow of a house a furious dog barked from within and Dédé sprang forward on his toes. He ran to the corner of Rue Pasteur and on turning into it began to sprint, attempting to outrun the heavy crunch of

145

each step on the grit. Another dog growled and ran to the end of its tether barking as he passed. Dédé swerved into the road at full pace with adrenalin coursing. Nearing the alley to his own road he slowed up and came to a halt hard against a telegraph pole. He turned back panting in the hot air expecting to see lights and vehicles and then moved into the shadow of the alley to observe again with his heart throbbing. He breathed heavily and felt the sweat on his skin as the cicadas filled the alley with their song. The hot air felt like it might burst.

Dédé returned home, extinguishing the noise of the cicadas as he passed. He lifted the rusty gate once more and tapped on the door.

"Ouvre la porte - c'est moi," he said gruffly.

Walking into the house dejected, he threw off his cap and without removing his boots, went straight to the bedroom. Paulette was on her side holding her stomach. She looked at him as he came into the lamplight.

"She won't come," he said.

Paulette said nothing. Their eyes locked for a second. They had no language to share their helplessness, but they did not need it. He dropped to the edge of the bed, whilst she shivered into a contraction. He held her hand.

"Va chercher Madame Berge," she said.

Sundries

Tess Tidey
Whiteford Rd
Horsham

Dearest Tess,

I hope that all is going well at home and at school? It has poured with rain today, so I decided to go and do boring jobs at the shops in Oakham. I was spurred out of the house by an emergency text from Sasha informing us that she had left her clarinet in the hallway. So, after my first little job as a clarinet-courier, I decided to get wet a second time on the high street in town.

The main reason for the visit was to call into Mill Street at a shop called Nature's Dispensary, which sells lotions, potions, lozenges, creams, capsules, sprays, balms, decoctions, oils, and unguents of all kinds. The quantity of small bottles crammed into the little shelves makes one dizzy, as I tried to match the long names on each bottle with those on my list. It is not long before I've given up and ask for help from the lady who lifts the flap of the counter and comes out to take charge of the search. We crouch low for a tub of capsules and I have to reach high for a little brown bottle of magnesium powder, brushing away a slight cobweb from a beam. Meanwhile, the rain outside has turned into a thunderstorm, sending sheets of water onto the glass shop-front. The lady closes the front door and we both complain about how humid it is in the low-ceilinged shop.

By now the only thing missing from the list is the Oregano Vulgare. According to the lady, this is a powerful oil that is kept with other similar items around the corner in the dispensary. She navigates the counter flap again whilst I look at a basket of breads and biscuits, but I catch a glimpse of her smile as she disappears into the dim-lit alcove as if exchanging silent greetings. In my mind's eye, I conjure a picture of a raven or jackdaw on a perch in the dispensary, its head cocked to one side, blinking at her as she smiles and nods back.

Black birds of this kind, you will understand, have names like Edgar or Mordecai or Magellan. Being cleverer than clever, they would never make themselves known whilst a customer is in the shop. I picture the raven's eye following the lady as she scans slowly along the shelves, passing the large jar containing a human brain and a smaller one with the brain of a lemur. There are similar pickles of mushrooms and chilli peppers and of newts of different types. Tall and short bottles of oils are arranged by colour from yellow to green to brown. A few are open on the dresser top where two large chopping boards are held back by an array of mortar and pestles and cork-stoppered jars of grey and white powders. All around hang sprigs of dried herbs and amongst them are desiccated songbirds dangling by string.

Once located, a large pipette is used to transfer the oregano oil from its jar to a tiny bottle. The lady wipes the rim, fixes the lid, nods politely to the raven and returns to the shop, placing it alongside the other purchases. Somehow in my reverie I have picked up a blueberry pie from the breads and cakes section and although shocked by the price, I take it to the counter.

"Is that everything?" the lady asks.

"Yes, I think so," I say, realising that it's going to be an expensive morning. A quick mental check of the price labels comes to about £100, so I continue hesitantly.

"I'm becoming a bit of a regular here, do you give any discount to your best customers?"

But she tells me that unfortunately she does not. A little saddened by this, I reach for my shopping bag pulling out my wallet and then a sealed white envelope containing the cash and change that you had raised for me at your cake sale in Horsham. I ask if it would be okay for me to pay partly in cash and the rest by card? The lady confirms that this would be fine.

"You see, my niece who is just ten raised the money in this envelope for me by organising a cake sale in Sussex," I went on.

"What a poppet," said the lady in a hushed voice.

Then she paused and looked onto the rain swept window, as if peering all the way to Sussex. The moment drifted on until I felt compelled to let out a little cough to remind her of my presence at the counter. The lady blinked.

"*I think* that a small discount *is* allowed in the circumstances."

She stopped strangely again, peered upwards for a moment as if seeking some invisible assistance. In that instant I heard something from the dispensary that might have been a wing beat.

"Yes!" exclaimed the Lady as if reaching an agreement. "I think that sixty-three pounds and *one penny* is about right, don't you?" She said slowly placing great emphasis on the single penny.

A little taken aback, I simply handed her the envelope saying that by a strange coincidence - all the money was therein. Then, I thanked her very much for her help and generosity, so that I could leave and get this down onto paper to you before the memory fades.

"Thank you again," I said as I left the shop. The lady formed another faint smile,
"What a poppet," she said.

I hope that you, Mummy and my other favourite niece Baby-Nell are all very well? I hope that Billie and Douglas-Dudley and the tortoises and the chickens are not pooing in every nook and cranny!

Keep up the running and thank you very much once again for arranging your cake sale and raising £63.01 to help me. I have special vitamins and minerals for a while now.

With my love.

Kannur Beach House,
Kerala,
India

Dear Nazir,

I can't help but chuckle as I type, picturing the bewildered expression that your face will probably show on opening this box.

I had reason to make one of my regular pilgrimages to our local hardware shop yesterday. You might recall me saying that this particular shop is an emporium of all things mechanical and practical - that rarely lets the customer down when searching for one kind of contraption or another. To borrow your words, it is the fanciest of 'fancy shops', and when it comes to finding things that will couple two objects together, it has no match, or so I thought. On arrival at the hardware store a recent memory was jogged of being at Kannur Beach House, discussing a device that would allow you to spin out your fishing net without it tangling. As I recall, the specification required the object to be able to turn freely whilst holding a minimum of 8kg.

Now, I remember conjuring an image in that moment of something sleek, light-weight, ergonomic and probably spherical, with a carabiner clip at both ends, that would help you to perfect your art during the dawn fishing ritual.

However, as with so many other things in life, there was nothing physical on offer to meet the mental picture that I had invented. Not to be beaten, I set about trying to fabricate a solution of my own from what was on display in the rows of cardboard boxes. In the process I've created something ugly, clunky, heavy and square that might, or might not, do the job. The only aspect that I'm confident in is that it will allow two objects - that's one human being and one casting net - to operate independently of each other. It will most definitely hold 8 to 10kg of weight. In fact, it would probably tow a broken-down oil tanker.

If it does not do the job, please find enclosed: two trolley wheels, two cleats and four bolts from halfway across the planet. Perhaps there will be alternative uses for them aboard the Ark that you are intending to build?

Lots of love to you, Rosie and Sunir

Dear Friends and Family,

Group emails are a poor show in my opinion, but I am indebted to so many of our friends and family for this trip to see the neurologist in Missouri, that it seems the only option.

Each of you has given invaluable support and I leave full of gratitude to you all. Whilst the medical adventure is still so fresh, I wanted to say an initial thank you. There's forty-five mins of heel-kicking in an airport, so I'll do my best.

There has been lots of talk of the royal wedding here. Many, from all walks of life will be tuning in very early on Saturday morning. I've told people that we are returning home today, because we have tickets to the evening reception. It's Ozark, Missouri and who knows what people believe? There is, for instance, an unnervingly wide misconception that London and England are one and the same thing. I'm guessing it would risky in a crowded place to proffer a view on what shape the Earth is. However, to a man and woman, everyone we have met has been courteous, warm, funny, cheerful and proud of their place in the world. There is a sense of togetherness that's almost palpable. In this quiet corner of America it feels apt that each new ten dollar bill has the phrase 'We The People' stained into the background.

In other important matters, there are chicken hawks here - that eat people's chickens. Then there are foxes, coyotes, possums and black snakes. We've seen lots of armadillos - but dead, like hedgehogs on the road. People call them dead-dillos. Aside from the greater array of deadly wildlife, Missouri looks and feels like our family's part of France, but on steroids. However, it's also as unmistakably American as eating a slice of apple pie at gun point. Everything is big, the bars are near pitch dark and as the famous film says: there's only two types of music - Country... and Western.

I had thirty blood tests yesterday, gave four little tubes of saliva and was poked with various mouth swabs. I'll be leaving about a quarter of myself here. We got on very well with the neurologist, spending nearly two hours with him during our initial session. He's detached and nerdy, diminutive in size, but is also muscle-bound. The overall sense is of an awkward, obsessive man, but one not lacking in kindness. He warmed rapidly on finding a patient who shared his negative views about the state of neurology in modern medicine and became almost chipper to find he could discuss MND right the way down the intra-cellular level.

He has assembled an expert team of therapists. We spent all day with them which was a tiring but excellent experience seeing a super physio, psychologist, nutritionist and energy medicine therapist! I'm certain that the overall package is pioneering.

The nurses in particular liked our Englishness. Also, they seemed motivated to work with people who are not scared of trying things out and with whom they could explore evolving ideas. I've just made it through airport security (another story in itself) with ten little metal discs glued up my back and down the right leg as the energy medicine specialist wanted to give these little stick-on batteries a go to see if they might improve nerve and muscle function in the way they do for nerve and muscle injuries.

So, we are tired but happy with the outcome and thankful for the big family effort and support of our friends too. Charlie has been great throughout, showing her usual strength (pushing a wheelchair stacked with suitcases), cheerfulness and fortitude.

Thank you so much everybody. I can never repay this kindness but wanted you at least to sense how grateful I am.

With love.

Ps - Just another little vignette:
Three nurses were busying themselves around me whilst taking blood. Two were also part-time farm girls at home. The youngest mentioned finding what she thought was an old tyre in the dimmed light of her chicken coop last week, which turned out to be a coiled black snake. I asked what she did next.
"Oh, I just shot it," she said.
"Wow," I said, "with a shotgun?"
"No stupid," she said,
"the shotgun would have made a mess of the coup. I shot it with the 22 rifle to make it clean...and besides the 45 Magnum's got too much recoil for my liking."
Only in America!

Cogitations

Don't Mention the Boomies

Baby Boomers piss me off. It's not just that they gave us a hole in the ozone layer, acid rain and Barry Manilow - it's more than that. Having lived through a time of peace and plenty, getting fat off jobs for life and ever rising property prices, the same generation of miscreant silver-surfers is now flailing against a world of globalisation and immigration that was their signature dish, whilst denying the climate crisis they did so much to create (and almost nothing to stop). Maybe as the baby boomers process into the afterlife on titanium hips, pulling golf carts or tossing garbage from cruise ships as they go, they might have paused, but as a last hurrah, whilst sitting atop generous pensions with lifestyles that their children and grandchildren will not know - they give us Donald Trump, in the hope that he might dismantle a world order that their parents sacrificed so much for.

To be fair, my generation, the generation that came after, has been lost, lame and lacklustre and has largely picked up the ladle from the same punch bowl, to continue on with the same party. And we all know that the millennials that follow us are entitled and feckless, but it's the baby boomers who get me going, because they still have the money, the good teeth and the numbers to keep screwing things up. It's an indictment to all of us adults, of any age, that a seventeen-year-old called Greta is now leading the charge to save us from ourselves. In defence of the baby boomers, it is true that each generation is doomed to be criticised by its successors. To borrow a quote from a wise friend, it is also true that we all live in one life-cycle that happens to coincide with one moment in history, but be that as it may, those baby boomers do seem to have made a colossal mess and in a wayward attempt to straighten things out have turned to a growing cast of strong-man grotesques called Donald and Boris and Vladimir, Victor and Recep, whose only playbook is to divide us...to rule us.

Baby boomers - the teenage generation that never grew up - are those born worldwide between 1946 and 1964. They followed the 'silent generation' who witnessed the world wars and preceded 'generation X', who have witnessed a lot of telly. Researching the baby-boomer dates was a relief, because it puts my parents and in-laws in the clear on a technicality (so that no Wills need to get changed as a result of this rant). It follows that the first baby boomers reached a retirement age of sixty-five around 2011. There are about eighty million boomers in the U.S, representing about thirty-one percent of the population. By and large, boomers have become the largest single voting bloc in the west since the eighties. In Canada, they are known as 'boomies', where over six million reside. In Britain, the same group is also known as the 'demographic bulge', because we Brits can never resist a bit of innuendo.

Baby boomers were the product of a world in turmoil. When many millions of service personnel returned to their homes from the Second World War and tens of millions of others, who had been displaced, moved around the planet in search of a new life free from conflict. Thus, the stage was set for some big changes in western societies.

America was of course the epicentre of the baby boom. As a generation of GIs, who had already been hardened by the poverty of the Great Depression returned home victorious, hardened again by wars on continents where communism was taking hold, the forward thinking 66th American Congress had already seen the threats and had acted decisively, by bringing in the GI Bill of Rights in June 1944, the same month as the D-day landings in Normandy. In so doing, they ushered in the American Dream. Loans for homes and farms were made available to GIs at low interest rates with no down payment and further education was suddenly and purposefully made a reachable goal for everyday people. With the stage set for a better life ahead, the young men and women who had defeated fascism were now given the altogether more agreeable task of making an army of babies, who would go onto unleash the full force of a new type of capitalism.

In the titanic tussle for ideological, military and economic superiority between communism and capitalism, this emerging generation became the west's most visible secret weapon. Forty years later, it was this new breed of carefree, western consumers who had inadvertently done more to see off communism than all the missiles and rockets ever built, by proving that whilst communism could give a county guns, capitalism could give a nation 'guns and butter' (plus rock'n'roll, electric meat carvers, space hoppers, microwave food, camping cars and soda streams). Unleashing the creative forces of a more focussed brand of capitalism and offering it up to a bright-eyed generation was a dead cert strategy for success. The 'flower power' movement, in the second half of the baby boom, cottoned on early to the obvious flaws in the new world equation, but this counter culture was never going to match the forces ranged against it, even before you add the bell-bottoms and floral print. Rarely has a movement become potent when it devotes much of its energies to tripping on mushrooms.

Fourteen years before the 66th US congress lit the long fuse for the Baby Boom, one of the most influential, but least celebrated members of the twentieth centuries cast, sat down to write an essay. John Maynard Keynes was a sober, British economist who wrote lengthy tomes about how economies, markets and societies function. His books on monetary and fiscal policy have tortured economics students ever since. Keynes was also quietly a member of the famous Bloomsbury Set of artists and intellectuals, suggesting a creative streak in the renowned economist. He must have felt a creative urge the day or evening that he pulled up a chair and began writing 'The Economic Possibilities of our Grandchildren'. As with great scientists, to be able to conceive something truly original involves being able to mix a keen intellect with a powerful imagination. Keynes and others had already understood free markets and free trade were not enough on their own to keep economies afloat, as the fuel moved around too erratically, causing the economic engine either to overheat or to stall altogether. But, if free trade and fast flowing money could be correctly mixed and channelled using a government's fiscal and monetary policy as the carburettor, the engine could run more smoothly, taking its passengers much further and faster. This economic engine could drive human progress at a rate that had not yet been seen. There were downsides of course, in that an ever-expanding

162

economy still needed an ever-growing base of workers to support it and an ever-larger mass of consumers to sustain it. Despite the improvements made by his economic theory, he was still helping to re-design what we would now call a pyramid scheme. However, the scheme was not aimed at shifting cosmetics or diet pills. It went on to underpin just about everything we did. In any event, in 1930, the world was considered so vast as to be almost inexhaustible. There was simply no prospect of running out of it.

I suspect that with restless ideas about his economic philosophy troubling the deep recesses of his mind, Keynes began a thought experiment one hundred years into the future as he wrote. The results were remarkable. In his mind, free market capitalism, coupled with his own Keynesian economics were a necessary, probably an essential ingredient, to stop economies continually slipping back into grinding depressions which would cause a predictable pattern of immense suffering. It was also a powerful antidote to the spectre of global, soviet style communism and provided a means to lift entire continents out of subsistence and poverty by shaking up the traditional order of things and turbocharging people's productivity wherever it went.

In his mind, as he followed his economic transformation around the globe into future decades, he was able to picture a time, only a century away from where he sat, when the project would be complete. Economies would be stable and prosperous. By this time, humankind would have done what was needed to lift itself away from scarcity and into comfort. It followed, that the next thing that we would do is to take our collective feet off the gas. In a world where even the workers were well housed, fed and clothed and where advancing technology was equipped to do most of the nasty stuff for us, we could kick back. In this world, he calculated that even the industrious would only need to work for eighteen hours a week. The human race would, at this stage, be able to devote its time and energies to the things that truly nourish us as beings - by expressing ourselves through culture, art, the natural world, scientific discovery and sport. Leisure and family time would be our new major occupation and how to fill the time peacefully and positively would be our greatest life challenge. At this time "the love of money… will be recognised for what it is, a somewhat disgusting morbidity". So thought the chief engineer of the economic thinking that has dominated ever since. The genie would go back into the bottle to make way for our more noble callings. For him, humanity must first travel through "the tunnel of economic necessity" that was capitalism, before emerging into "daylight". All of this would come to fruition by 2030.

Fifty years on and half way through Keynes' timeline, it was 1980. The baby boomers were taking over the reins from the silent generation and the boom was only just beginning to hit full swing. By then boomers had got a taste for speed in every area conceivable. Fast food, fast cars, fast fashion, fast moving consumer goods, and jet travel were now nearly ubiquitous in the prospering west. With generation X as kids in tow - we were all at it and all know the rest of the story. We became more rapacious, just at the moment where we might have taken stock and become the more noble figures that Keynes had envisioned.
Automation did not make us work less. We began to work more, as the shrinking globe began to spin faster. Then,

164

income inequality began to move in the wrong direction too, before diverging by a staggering 278% over a couple of decades. Computers didn't replace paper, as junk mail spewed through our letterboxes and families were not troubled by what to do in their leisure time as we split up and followed our jobs to wherever they took us, whilst the divorce rates also soared.

Like ripples from a great stone thrown into a pond, I have benefitted a great deal from the continuing baby boom era and everything that has come with it. I clambered aboard and saw the value of every property I've owned soar. I can't resist a £3 T-shirt, have flown on many airplanes and have eaten a small herd of cows from head to hoof. But like coming to a party late, where the guests are already drunk, where the tables are sticky and where the salad looks fingered and wilted - it's been an uneasy experience. I've tutted at the mess, have wanted to take the car keys out of the reveller's pockets, to put the empties in the recycling and to turn the music down so that I could hear myself think. What a kill joy. When I lived in Paris for a while, I used to drink beer with another English guy called Harry. He was working the till of a bureau de change on the Rue de Rivoli on his gap year before starting an accountancy degree. He unburdened himself one evening about a problem that had dogged his adolescence. His yuppy parents were cooler than him. They were unrestrained party goers who'd pick him up from school in a noisy sports car and who had poured scorn on his choice of summer job, when he could have taken off to the other side of the world and gone on a six-month bender. For him, this was an affliction and I kind of get it.

165

The climate may be in crisis, our soils may be exhausted, the sea awash with plastic and half stripped of its life in a world where even the insects have not avoided becoming extinct en masse, but I'm also reminded of a well quoted sequence in the Life of Brian movie, when John Cleese (playing Reg the militant Jewish shop-steward) asks, "What have the Romans ever done for us?"
After some back and forth with his comrades he concludes, "All right, but apart from the sanitation, the medicine, education, wine, public order, irrigation, roads, a fresh water system, and public health…what have the Romans ever done for us?"

And so it has been for the baby boomers, for whom it also really has been one heck of a productive party too. First of all - and contrary to even many of their own expectations, they avoided nuclear war on their watch. Meanwhile, they've built the tallest buildings, dug the deepest holes and made the longest tunnels, stretching physics to its limit. They've first imagined and then brought into existence the most mind-boggling technology and on the way have taken billions out of poverty, extending their own and their forebears' lifespans too. They've been to the moon and looked down on how they have re-engineered parts of the planet for habitation and food. They have explored the solar system and have theorised about the origins of the universe, just as they discovered the strange quantum world of the very small. They've taken risks and have worked feverishly to cure diseases, sequence the genome, clone animals, and will leave behind the most sensational back catalogue of music and cinema. Boomers have gone from analogue to digital, from pub skittles and slide rules, to the internet and quantum processors. They have evolved from no

166

computing, to home computing, to cloud computing. It's been a trip from no phones to smart phones, from Pong - the two-line ping-pong game on a TV, to Grand Theft Auto. They brought us into being and doted on us as kids, whilst building the welfare state across Europe. Most amazing of all, they've done all of this whilst largely intoxicated.

Writing about the past is not so hard. Deciphering the present is only a fraction more difficult if one tries to keep on top of things. This summer, I've watched on as fires raged in the arctic circle for a full three months, as one month of melting on the Greenland ice sheet has raised the global sea level and as the Amazon has burned at unprecedented rates. However, last month a company announced that it had designed a solar panel that could also desalinate water and only this week 180 of America's largest corporations confirmed that their chief aim was no longer to provide profits for their shareholders at all costs, but instead to improve society. The signs are shocking, but perhaps it's all still in the balance?

So, who's going to clear up after the baby boom party? Are the current, more junior generations, so satiated on Netflix and chicken, going to be up to the job? And if we do summon the collective strength to clear up the debris, replace the carpets, redecorate and reseed the lawns - will the celestial man from the council turn up with a clip board and declare the venue unfit for habitation anyway?

167

To Be or Not To Be

This year, a man called Paul Lamb took a legal case through the High Court and onto the Court of Appeal in a story that made barely a ripple of news. Paul's back was broken in a motorcycle accident thirty years ago, leaving him almost totally paralysed from the neck down. If this is not bad enough, the nature of the injury involves near constant pain. Paul has had his fill of the unending suffering and for the last decade has been seeking to find a way of ending his life - whilst successive governments and our legal system have done their utmost to stop him. Committing suicide is not illegal. It was decriminalised in England and Wales sixty years ago but has never been a crime in Scotland. In modern times, a person who is revived after attempting suicide is no longer prosecuted and imprisoned. Up until this point, religious objections had held sway on the laws governing suicide. St Augustine and Thomas Aquinas had set out that, whoever deliberately took away the life given to them by their Creator showed the utmost disregard for the will of God and jeopardised their own salvation. With sanctity of life as the watchword, the Church of England thus considered suicide a sin, with abortion being at the other end of this moral dumbbell. The law of the land fell in with these views until 1961. 'Suiciding' other people is however illegal, because that's a potential euphemism for murder. The logic here demands

169

that we are protected from being unwittingly or unwillingly suicided. Step forward Article 2 of 1961 Suicide Act which does just that, by making it a serious criminal offence for anyone to help a person commit suicide. So that we can all sleep more soundly in our beds, the tariff for suiciding someone else is fourteen years of prison time. So far so good, but what happens when a person wants to commit suicide but can't do it on their own? Then, like Paul Lamb, one is trying to undertake a legal act, but is recruiting an illegal actor to achieve the result, making the person who helped a criminal.

In the autumn, an eighty-one-year-old great grandmother with the suitably grandmotherly name of Mavis Ecclestone was acquitted of murder and manslaughter. Mavis gave her terminally ill husband Dennis a lethal cocktail of prescription medication before downing the mixture herself. A fourteen-page suicide note told why the couple, who had been married for almost sixty years, were ending their lives. Dennis Ecclestone had been diagnosed with bowel cancer some three years earlier and was subject to a 'Do not resuscitate order'. Mavis, however, was not and was able to be revived. Mr Eccleston passed away while holding hands with his wife in adjoining hospital beds. She said he shed a tear and died just after she reminded him of their first kiss back in 1958. Her heartbroken family claim she was arrested and kept in a police cell for thirty hours wearing the same nightie, dressing gown and slippers she had had on in hospital, and that officers denied her access to a toilet.

The Crown had alleged that the couple had not formed a 'clear and common' agreement to end their own lives and even so, that it being a 'mercy killing' was no defence to Mrs Eccleston's actions, because the law does not recognise

the term. Mrs Eccleston said her husband had "begged" for her help to end his life and given her instructions how to do it. She said she told him,
"If that's the way you are going then I am coming too".
After a public outcry and some stalwart media work by her daughter, Joy, Mavis was cleared of any wrongdoing after a two-week trial at Stafford Crown Court.

Before we go much further, I need to put in a couple of provisos. First things first, I'm not an authority on this subject and secondly, I'm afraid that there is a need to go into the terminology that's used in this debate, lest we trip and stumble on the syntax further down. You may need to turn the telly down for the paragraph ahead. In this context, *terminally ill* is a phrase used to describe a person who has been given less than six months to live by specialist doctors, whilst *incurably suffering* is used to describe a person in the awful situation of Paul Lamb, who is not expected to die any time soon, but who is suffering without any prospect of improvement or cure. Wikipedia tells me that Euthanasia simply means a 'good death' in Greek, but it expands by saying that there are three subsets. Fortunately, for those of us with limited mental capacity, *Involuntary Euthanasia* is murder, leaving just voluntary or non-voluntary euthanasia to grapple with. *Non-voluntary Euthanasia* is conducted when the consent of the patient is unavailable (for instance, when the person might be in a vegetative state) whereas *Voluntary euthanasia* is conducted with the consent of the patient. To muddle things, the terms *active* and *passive* are also used. Passive involves 'pulling a plug' or withdrawing treatment, whilst active involves doing something specific to bring life to an end. To make matters harder still, legal definitions across jurisdictions differ too, but we won't go there. In Belgium, Luxembourg and the Netherlands, euthanasia is defined as 'termination of life by a doctor at the request of a patient'. This is a much wider approach than the definition of *assisted dying or assisted suicide,* which refer to the same thing and are limited to providing assistance to people who are terminally ill. *Mercy killing* is not a recognised phrase in law or medicine, but it does help to sell newspapers. Clear?!

Definitions aside, at one end of the spectrum the self-same activity is considered by some as killing whereas by others, it is considered as compassion. This spectrum is superbly reflected by the campaign groups that operate at either end of the debate. At one end is the tub-thumping pressure group named Care not Killing which is man marked by an earnest, liberal campaign group called Dignity in Dying. This sets the stage for a never-ending back and forth on the topic. If it helps, just picture the video-game avatars of Ian Paisley and Germaine Greer slugging it out in an eternal fist-fight. As the law currently criminalises all forms of assisted dying, Care not Killing has the self-appointed job of holding the line, so that we do not all go to hell in a handcart, whereas Dignity in Dying has a mission of reaching the next level, by reforming the current law, so that terminally ill people with less than six months to live can have a choice to end their lives in a time and way of their choosing. The quickest thinking among you will have noticed that Paul Lamb would not fit into the above category.

Care not Killing, presents its arguments in the following way. If the absolute ban against assisted dying is removed, this will be the start of 'a slippery slope'. Initially, just the helpers of a narrow band of terminally ill individuals might qualify for protection against prosecution if they assist a loved one or patient to end their life, but over time the categories of eligible people will naturally expand allowing ever wider groups to take up the opportunity. The first of these groups would probably be people like Paul who are incurably suffering. The inexorable expansion will therefore have a corrosive effect on society by putting pressure on the sick, disabled, needy, frail, and old to sign up for a one-way ticket. The premise is that those who no longer feel valuable will consider themselves useless and ask for the chop. This potent argument dovetails with a second one. People who are 'weak and vulnerable' will be at risk of being manipulated by others into seeking to end their own lives, because they are either a burden, have assets that can be inherited… or both.

These arguments are emotive and are worthy of some serious consideration. It's not accidental, however, that both conjure immediate mental frames in our minds. This might be a picture of the rapacious grandson encouraging his elderly grandmother to seek an assisted death, because the four-bedroomed detached house bordering Richmond Park is worth a bomb. Or one might conjure a severely disabled person watching TV, looking at a world from which they are separated, feeling a burden to everyone in their lives and considering ending it all - because the law now permits it. These, and many other similar stereotypes sit within the mental roll call of characters who exist in our mind's-eye, all drawn from those who have influenced our imaginations, such as Charles Dickens.

Powerful though they are, we should look at these arguments a little more closely and once done, examine the evidence for them. The basis of the slippery slope argument is that the law will be expanded over time to include ever larger groups of people. As said, it is a theoretical argument that packs a punch. It would be great if we could test the veracity of the theory. The good news is that we can. Back in 1997 Oregon became the first of ten states in the USA to legalise assisted dying for terminally ill people. Oregon's assisted dying laws have formed the template for the nine other permissive states. It's been twenty-two years since the law was enacted and it has not been extended beyond terminally ill adults. In Canada, where assisted dying for the terminally ill was adopted in 2016, the story is different. Here, the law is being challenged so that it is extended to include people who are incurably suffering too. This could be used as evidence of the slippery slope in action, but for my money it isn't. For decades those who have been campaigning for assisted dying have been arguing amongst themselves about whether incurably suffering people should be inside or outside the boundary. It's therefore no surprise that this long running disagreement continues to bubble. We can however probably use the well-known case of Switzerland as the clincher here. Laws allowing for limited assisting suicide were passed there in 1942 and have remained stable since. If there is a slope to be slipped down, surely the slide would have started at some point during the last eight decades? If the slippery slope was the major issue that it is painted to be, over such a long passage of time one might expect that waking up with just a toothache in Bern or Zürich would provide sufficient context for a trip to Dignitas.

Moving back to Oregon and applying the 'weak and vulnerable' argument is also illuminating. Here, no known abuse of the system has taken place since 1997. Back in Canada, there have already been occasions where case reviews have had to take place, of the new law that was only enacted in 2016. This is initially very concerning, but when looked at closely, rather than demonstrate the weak and vulnerable argument in action, it does the opposite, because on these occasions it has been the short-cutting of the stringent medical safeguards that has been spotted. The argument can be made therefore that the system to protect weak and vulnerable people is in fact working, because the safeguards are being actively policed.

It would be difficult to find someone totally impartial to adjudicate on these arguments, but I'm told that the balance of evidence weighs heavily against the slippery slope and weak and vulnerable arguments when they are looked at in practice.

As an aside, much of the focus when discussing this topic stays squarely within these shores. When we do look to the outside world our gaze rarely stretches further than Switzerland, because it's home to Dignitas - where desperate, but wealthier, terminally ill Brits go for a compassionate death. Occasionally the national debate looks across the sea to the Netherlands and considers the very differently conceived law on euthanasia. It therefore becomes easy to characterise assisted dying as a foible of the suspiciously secretive Swiss or euthanasia as a fetish of the alarmingly liberal Dutch, when it is really our cultural cousins in the United States and Canada to whom we might be better to look? Australia is following suit too. The state of Victoria legalised assisted dying in 2019 in an exercise that is expected to be mirrored by the other states over time. New Zealand's parliament has already passed legislation which will be voted on in a confirmatory referendum. As well as the cultural proximity in history, language and outlook, it is worth noting that these countries all share our Common Law legal system, thereby proving that our law is quite capable of dealing with this problem, when there is enough political will to solve it.

As mentioned, Care not Killing leads with these slippery slope and weak and vulnerable arguments, but I'm not alone in thinking that they are a smokescreen for more fundamental religious views about - you guessed it - the Sanctity of Life. There are three reasons in my humble, but skewed view, why the Sanctity of Life argument should no longer underpin the thinking on this side of the debate. We have already trailed the first and foremost of these. The decriminalising of suicide put the Sanctity of Life argument to bed in the sixties. In so doing one of the last elements of theocracy was removed from our democracy. It's only the moral and ethical complexity of assisted dying that has allowed supporters of the Sanctity of Life argument to keep a hidden, but religiously motivated toe hold within the legal system.

Perhaps slightly less pertinently, I object to the Sanctity of Life argument in a general sense too, because it rose from religious fervour and remains an article of faith held by the same belief systems, be they Christian or Muslim, that so regularly spawn indiscriminate death through persecution and war. Even taking religion out of the equation for a second, never has a species massacred its members with such gusto as our own. Religious or not, we generally have such little respect for life per-se in every other aspect of the world we inhabit, of animals large and small, of our land

and seas and every living thing which sustains us - that being so touchy about our own sanctity is an absurd conceit. Let's face it, if you were an alien surveying the industrial slaughter of the living things on Earth, from trees to chickens to elephants, you'd be forgiven for wondering what the fuss is about when letting go of a few poorly humans as they near the end of their lives.

The slippery slope and weak and vulnerable arguments, acting as a smokescreen for the Sanctity of Life belief, create a lot of foam and froth. They are not red herrings, but these noisy topics have often kept the public and our politicians away from the subtler issues that really do need to be reconciled if we are ever to find the right resolution to the problem of assisted dying.

We can deal with the legal issues succinctly. You will know that Parliament makes our laws and once made it is the job of the courts to interpret and uphold them. The current law is a blanket ban on assisted suicide. If it is to be reformed, it is Parliament's job to come up with something better and to replace it. Despite nine out of ten members of the public supporting a change in law, politicians do not like giving time to tricky problems that do not have any votes attached to them. To some degree, that would be that if it were not for the Human Rights Act. This international treaty has been brought into our national legislation. It creates a conundrum for our legal and political systems, because it sets a benchmark against which other bits of older domestic legislation can be measured. The Human Rights Act warms the cockles of a Guardian reader's heart as he picks the oats from his beard over the breakfast granola, but infuriates the Telegraph reader who would gladly take it outside and horsewhip it.

177

For supporters of assisted dying, the Human Rights Act provides the legal platform to ask the question: Does the blanket ban against assisted dying prevent me from using my right to self-determination, which is a central plank of the Human Rights Act? Equally, is the state's duty to protect life in the wrong, if a terminally ill person's only, realistic, legal options are to:

1. suffer a terrible illness,
2. commit suicide legally by taking action only whilst one is well enough to commit the act alone, or
3. go abroad for an assisted death whilst a person is still fit enough to travel?

These and other variants of the same questions are brought to the UK courts year in and year out by terminally ill and incurably suffering individuals. Using Canada as the example once again, the courts looked at these arguments and then considered the evidence for and against assisted dying, before ruling that its own blanket ban did infringe the human rights of terminally ill Canadians.

The medical ethics that surround assisted dying are perhaps the most nuanced and important aspect of the whole debate. Should doctors, who have sworn the Hippocratic oath to protect life and 'do no harm', play any role in ending life? Conversely, should doctors respect the views of those in their care and be allowed to help end the suffering of a terminally ill or incurably suffering patient?

Some might ask if a quiet and informal practice already exists in doctoring anyway that delivers most of what is needed, in all but name? Once upon a time it may have been the visiting family GP who gave your ninety-four-year-old granddad something to help make the pain go away and to help him sleep, into eternity. Ironically it was the repercussions from the inquiry about Harold Shipman, our nation's most prolific mass murderer, that shone a light on this practice and largely stopped it. However, does a modern-day version of end-of-life 'help' by doctors continue in hospitals and hospices? For instance, if a palliative doctor can increase the dose of a painkiller to alleviate physical suffering in the knowledge that this could hasten death, haven't we arrived at an entry level form of assisted dying anyway, but via a different route? If you know your way around the system a person can refuse treatment or have treatment withdrawn, requesting palliative care in its place. On top of all of this, would introducing assisted dying lead to a reduction in funding for palliative care and might drug companies invest less to find treatments for incurable diseases?

To reiterate, these are amongst the most important aspects to consider. Fortunately, I'm not going to try to attempt to deal with them in detail because the moral, ethical and technical subtleties are above my pay grade, but there are a couple of general things to point out.

Once again, these can be drawn from the evidence and not the arguments. Of the three palliative care systems that are ranked most highly in the world, two are in countries that permit assisted dying. For a long while, all of the major bodies who represent medical professionals in the UK objected to assisted dying. However, in 2008 the Royal College of Nursing moved its position to neutral, followed by the Royal College of Physicians in 2019 who did the same. As I write, the Royal College of GPs is counting the votes on a ballot about this topic and the British Medical Association is poised to canvass its own members this year. Nobody expects any of the medical associations to move in favour of assisted dying. This is considered a bridge too far, because it would inflame members with powerful religious convictions, but if either body or both change from objecting to a neutral position, it will signal that a tipping point has been reached within the medical establishment. We should still be cautious, because the Association of Palliative Care Medicine is unlikely to be changing its opinion in the short-term. These doctors are right at the sharp end of the problem and should have a greater say than the others. There are serious ethical objections, but palliative care doctors are often working in inadequately funded organisations, relying on charitable donations and many are also in the employ of hospices that arise from the Christian tradition, named after saints like St Luke, St Barnabas, St Catherine and many more.

Strangely, advancing medical technology may not always be on the plus side of the medical balance sheet either. There's no conspiracy here, but there is a nexus. Humankind now routinely uses modern medicine to extend lives that would otherwise be cut short. An amazing proportion of people reading this will have had a drug, therapy, procedure or operation that has improved and extended their lives. Without it, many of us would no longer be here at all. Medicine is perhaps the greatest triumph of our kind, but like space travel, it has no end. In 2015, Professor Stuart Kim of Stanford University confidently predicted that the first human to live to two hundred years of age has already be born. That's very cool, to a point, as long as we don't conflate living longer lives as a proxy for living better ones.

It may be distasteful to say it, but it is financially advantageous to use medical technology to keep people alive longer. When the life of an old or poorly person who has complex care needs is prolonged, there's a financial multiplier effect as multiple arms of the pharma and health sectors step in to administer services at the same time - in a kind of healthcare feeding frenzy. As already said, this makes sense when the result leads to a longer life that retains some vestiges of quality about it. If it doesn't, then one has to ask a question about who the real beneficiaries are from squeezing some further time out of a dying person's life. In this scenario, if the person no longer really wants to live anyway, then they can become more a victim than a patient.

I have recently read excerpts of a report that attempts to quantify the numbers of unpleasant deaths that occur in hospitals and hospices across the UK each year. A summary of types of bad death were illustrated to set the scene. There is a strong public education element to the report as it seeks to underline that many thousands of deaths that happen are not the painless or spiritual ones that we all hope for. If I could un-read these examples of bad types of dying, I surely would, but unfortunately, it's not possible to rub out phrases such as "vomiting your own faeces" once they've entered the imagination, like ghosts intent on doing a little haunting. The hope is that this report will help spark a debate about how we might all prefer to die, which will in turn unlock the stalemate on assisted dying for the terminally ill.

You don't have to be an immensely deep thinker to be struck by an anomaly in the assisted dying debate, which should not be dismissed by the experts as lightly as it often is. It stems from the often-used phrase, "you would not let your dog suffer like that". In reality, we often care for our pets every bit as much as we do for our human companions.

181

These, our dogs and cats, are the very creatures for whom we have to sum up the courage to let go of when they are too old or suffering hopelessly - by putting them to sleep. It is not wrong for opponents to stress major differences between poorly human beings and taking our ailing pets to see the vet. At the vets, we make decisions on behalf of our pets to save them from suffering, because they do not have the wherewithal to weigh up the situation, make a decision and then inject themselves with something lethal, although there is the chance that we will see this clip on YouTube someday. This point is a fair one. But the differences aside, when a person does not have the capacity to do the deed, but has weighed-up and understood a hopeless situation and made a decision, why shouldn't they also be allowed to end their own suffering and be put to sleep too?

To elevate my own conclusion on the subject from the veterinary world, it might be better to end by paraphrasing recent words from the Chief Executive Officer of Marie Curie Cancer Care. For a variety of misconceived reasons, "we place far too much emphasis on keeping people alive at any cost and far too little emphasis on enabling a good death". I'm told by a friend in Ireland that the Celtic tradition places emphasis on a good death. A life snatched away suddenly or violently is to be mourned. A life with a long, suffering departure is to be mourned. A good death is to be celebrated.

Terminally ill or incurably suffering people should not be denied a good death, just because they need help to do the deed. We boast a top-class legal system. Healthcare in Britain is the envy of much of the world. Combined, they are well capable of overseeing a set of safeguards that protect all of us. The public is staunchly in favour of change and our medical institutions are shifting their opinion. Not for the first time, it is our politicians who are behind the curve.

But let's not end on a downer.

To one and to all, I wish you a good death.

Acknowledgements

A team effort is needed even for a little book, such as this one. It would have been a botched job without the proofreading help of Matt Drakard, Vaccy Harrison and Charlotte Newby. Vaccy in particular has worked intensively to exorcise sloppy prose, to un-split infinitives, and to weed out a multitude of errors with her keen eye and attention to detail.

Meanwhile, the marvellous Olive Travers has encouraged and edited and occasionally restrained a couple of my more impulsive literary urges.

Praise is also due to Jessica Newby for the duck-whispering skills that provided the cover photograph of the quizzical duck.

As anyone who comes into contact with us is aware, this book, or anything else in my world would not happen at all, if it were not for Charlie.

My thanks to you all.

PN